Workbook

to accompany

Business Statistics

Richard P. Runyon

Audrey Haber

1982

Richard D. Irwin, Inc.
Homewood, Illinois

Printed in the United States of America.

ISBN 0-256-02737-4

1 2 3 4 5 6 7 8 9 K 9 8 7 6 5 4 3 2

Contents

Preface

This Study Guide provides additional guided practice in each of the statistical procedures appearing in the text. It also augments the text by introducing additional explanatory materials and topics or, in some cases, by presenting statistical procedures that are useful in specialized applications. In addition, the answers to the exercises provided in the text are given in greater detail. Thus you are able to see more than the bottom line, since various intermediate steps are included.

Deepest appreciation to Mindy Jassenoff who struggled her way through a sea of numbers and still managed to type a coherent manuscript.

This Study Guide is dedicated to our fathers and mothers.

Summation Notation

Throughout the text, you will be required to calculate the sum of various sets of numbers. Rather than providing verbal instructions such as "Sum all of the values of the X-variable", we shall use symbolic shorthand. The Greek capital letter Σ (sigma) instructs us to find the sum. If the variable, X, has the values of 4, 9, 12, 15, 21, then $\Sigma X = 61$. Similarly, if the cost of a gallon of gasoline at three service stations is \$1.42, \$1.37, and \$1.29, then $\Sigma X = \$4.08$.

Example A   Find ΣX, $(\Sigma X)^2$, and ΣX^2 of the following values of X: 1, 3, 6, 7

Solution
$$\Sigma X = 1 + 3 + 6 + 7 = 17$$
$$(\Sigma X)^2 = 17^2 = 289$$
$$\Sigma X^2 = 1^2 + 3^2 + 6^2 + 7^2$$
$$= 1 + 9 + 36 + 49$$
$$= 95$$

There are times when we do not wish to sum all of the values of a variable but only a selected subset. We use subscripts to indicate which values are to be summed. Thus if $X_1 = 3$, $X_2 = 5$, $X_3 = 6$, $X_4 = 8$, $X_5 = 10$, $X_6 = 13$ and we wish to sum X_2 through X_4, the notation would read:

$$\sum_{i=2}^{4} X_i$$

Verbally, this notation tells us: sum all of the values of the X variable beginning with the second (i = 2) through the fourth (i = 4). In this example, then

$$\sum_{i=2}^{4} X_1 = X_2 + X_3 + X_4 = 5 + 6 + 8 = 19$$

Example B   Find each of the following, given the values of the X-variable:

$$X_1 = 2, X_2 = 5, X_3 = 6, X_4 = 8, X_5 = 10, X_6 = 11, X_7 = 12, X_8 = 15, X_9 = 16$$

(a) $\displaystyle\sum_{i=2}^{8} X_i$ $67 = 5 + 6 + 8 + 10 + 11 + 12 + 15$

(b) $\displaystyle\left(\sum_{i=2}^{8} X_i\right)^2$ X_i $4489 = (5 + 6 + 8 + 10 + 11 + 12 + 15)^2 = (67)^2$

(c) $\displaystyle\sum_{i=2}^{8} X_i^2 = 5^2 + 6^2 + 8^2 + 10^2 + 11^2 + 12^2 + 15^2 =$
$25 + 36 + 64 + 100 + 121 + 144 + 225 = 715$

(d) $\displaystyle\sum_{i=3}^{n} X_i$ in which n is the final value of X.
$6 + 8 + 10 + 11 + 12 + 15 + 16 = 78$

Solution

(a) $\displaystyle\sum_{i=2}^{8} X_i = 5 + 6 + 8 + 10 + 11 + 12 + 15 = 67$

(b) $\displaystyle\left(\sum_{i=2}^{8} X_i\right)^2 = (67)^2 = 4,489$

(c) $\displaystyle\sum_{i=2}^{8} X_i^2 = 5^2 + 6^2 + 8^2 + 10^2 + 11^2 + 12^2 + 15^2 = 715$

(d) $\displaystyle\sum_{i=3}^{n} X_i = 6 + 8 + 10 + 11 + 12 + 15 + 16 = 78$

Summation Rules

(1) The sum of a constant added together n times equal n times that constant:

$$\sum_{i=1}^{n} c = nc$$

For example, let c be a constant (c = 4) and n = 6. Thus,

$$\sum_{i=1}^{n} c = (4 + 4 + 4 + 4 + 4 + 4) = 6(4) = 24.$$

Example C   Let $\overline{X}$ be the constant, $\overline{X} = 11$, n = 5

$$\sum_{i=1}^{n} \overline{X} = n\overline{X} = 5(11) = 55$$

[Recall formula (3.1):

$$\overline{X} = \frac{\Sigma X}{n},$$

Thus, $n\overline{X} = \Sigma X$. Thus, $n\overline{X}$. In this example, $n\overline{X} = 55 = \Sigma X$. Therefore, given the values of n and $\overline{X}$, we may find ΣX].

(2) The sum of a constant times each value of a variable equals the sum of the variable times that constant:

$$\sum_{i=1}^{n} cX_i = c\sum_{i=1}^{n} X_i$$

Let c = 4, $X_1 = 1$, $X_2 = 3$, $X_3 = 6$

$$\sum_{i=1}^{n} cX_i = 4(1+3+6) = 4(10) = 40$$

A Word of Caution

The sum of the values of a variable squared is *not* equal to the sum of the squares of that variable, i.e.,

$$\left(\sum_{i=1}^{n} X_i\right)^2 \neq \sum_{i=1}^{n} X_i^2$$

Let $X_1 = 1$, $X_2 = 3$, $X_3 = 6$

$$\left(\sum_{i=1}^{n} X_i\right)^2 = (1 + 3 + 6)^2 = 10^2 = 100$$

$$\sum_{i=1}^{n} X_i^2 = 1^2 + 3^2 + 6^2 = 1 + 9 + 36 = 46$$

$$100 \neq 46$$

Double Summation

There are numerous occasions when data are arranged in a table consisting of rows and columns. The subscripts *i* and *j* are often used to indicate the row and column respectively. In symbolic shorthand, the first subscript identifies the row number and the second the column number.

$$\sum_{i=1}^{n} \sum_{j=1}^{n} X_{i,j}$$ tells you to set the first index

equal to its first value (i=1) and let the second index run through its range (j=1 through n); then set the first index equal to its second value (i=2) and let the second index run through its range again (j=1 through n), etc.

Example D   Given the price per pound of three items at two different supermarkets:

Items (i)	Supermarket (j)	
	1	2
1	0.80	0.75
2	0.21	0.19
3	0.66	0.52

$$\sum_{i=1}^{n} \sum_{j=1}^{n} X_{i,j}$$

(1)   i=1, j=1 through n
     0.80 + 0.75 +

(2)   i=2, j=1 through n
     0.21 + 0.19 +

(3)   i=3, j=1 through n
     0.66 + 0.52

or, $$\sum_{i=1}^{n} \sum_{j=1}^{n} X_{i,j} = 0.80 + 0.75 + 0.21 + 0.19 + 0.66 + 0.52 = 3.13$$

The notation for the preceding table is shown below:

Item (i)	Supermarket (j)		Sums
	1	2	
1	$X_{1,1}$	$X_{1,2}$	$\sum_{j=1}^{2} X_{1,j}$
2	$X_{2,1}$	$X_{2,2}$	$\sum_{j=1}^{1} X_{2,j}$
3	$X_{3,1}$	$X_{3,2}$	$\sum_{j=1}^{2} X_{3,j}$
Sums	$\sum_{i=1}^{3} X_{i,1}$	$\sum_{i=1}^{3} X_{i,2}$	$\sum_{i=1}^{3} \sum_{j=1}^{2} X_{i,j}$

Example E   Given the following data table, find:

(a) $\sum\limits_{i=1}^{3} X_{i,2}$

(b) $\sum\limits_{j=2}^{4} X_{3,j}$

(c) $\sum\limits_{i=1}^{3} \sum\limits_{j=1}^{4} X_{i,j}$

	Columns (j)			
Rows (i)	1	2	3	4
1	11	9	8	6
2	7	4	5	10
3	13	2	3	15

Solution

(a) $\sum\limits_{i=1}^{3} X_{i,2} = 9 + 4 + 2 = 15$

(b) $\sum\limits_{j=2}^{4} X_{3,j} = 2 + 3 + 15 = 20$

(c) $\sum\limits_{i=1}^{3} \sum\limits_{j=1}^{4} X_{i,j} = 11 + 9 + 8 + 6 + 7 + 4 + 5 + 10 + 13 + 2 + 3 + 15 = 93$

"Now that we've learned to talk, what should we do about the economy?"

Chapter 1

Lesson 1-1 Statistics and Uncertainty

The opening scenario deals with a problem whose scope is unknown. In the relatively few cases where computer fraud has been discovered, the amounts of money lost, either directly or through loss of services, has frequently been in the many thousands of dollars.

Computer fraud was selected in the opening chapter for a variety of reasons:

1. There is much uncertainty concerning the incidence of computer crimes. This is primarily due to the fact that they are committed by brilliant individuals, often with no more motivation than to "beat the system."

2. The usual methods of crime detection are often to no avail. In a cleverly executed crime, the books will balance. For example, in the salami technique executed in the scenario, a small amount is skimmed off all or a selected number of accounts and is assigned to the criminal's account.

3. Evidence of a crime is often destroyed in a fraction of a second after the fraud is perpetuated. Company executives may be left with an uneasy feeling that the profit picture is not as good as expected but be unable to advance a satisfactory explanation.

4. Even when computer fraud is discovered, it may be covered up out of a sense of embarrassment or in order to avoid stockholders' displeasure.

5. Law enforcement personnel, from police and district attorneys, are reluctant to prosecute computer crime suspects because of their own limited knowledge of computer technology and a fear that the defense will make monkeys out of them in the courtroom.

Two broad areas in which statistical has a potential use are:

1. *In the detection of a specific crime.* Montana Rincon was using statistics with this goal in mind. His strategy was to obtain a large random sample from the population and exhaustively analyze the accounts in the sample. Descriptive statistics calculated from the sample would yield summary statements concerning unexplained errors in the sample. The use of inferential statistics would permit him to make estimates concerning the extent of these errors in all five million accounts. Further sleuthing would reveal whether or not these errors were genuine mistakes or instances of fraud.

2. *To obtain better estimates of the incidence of computer crime in the total population of all organizations using computer technology.* To date, estimates are little more than informed guesses. Think about how one might go about obtaining estimates of the extent of computer crime within a given business or industry. How would the population be defined? How would the sample be collected? What assorted data would be analyzed? Clearly one technique that is ruled out would be an interview of individuals intimately involved in computer crime. You wouldn't for example, select a random sample of computer programmers and ask them "Have you committed any sort of computer crime or are you in the process of committing computer crime right now?"

    We should also note that all computer crime does not involve the illegal transfer of money. Sometimes goods are illegally transferred. At these times, goods, or services are billed but not delivered. However, the computer read-out would show all transactions were completed.

Lesson 1-2 Populations and Sources

Some statisticians prefer to define populations only in terms of values of a variable. Thus, if we were interested in the average weekly take-home pay of workers in a given industry, the population would consist of wages paid to all employees. The wages would be the population and the employees would be the sources of the population. The following shows some typical populations and sources:

Sources	*Populations*
Eligible voters	Yes and No votes
1982 Model Cars	Miles per gallon rating of all cars
Graduating Class at a given University	The quality point average of all the students
Stocks listed at the New York Stock Exchange	The value of a share of each stock

Most statisticians do not differentiate between sources and populations. Thus, they are willing to identify "all eligible voters" and "how all eligible voters cast their ballots" as populations. This slight ambiguity does not usually pose any difficulties as long as we are aware of the fact that statistical statements are based on numerical values. Thus, an inference about a population results in numerical statements. For example, 53 percent of the eligible voters are registered Democrats.

Lesson 1-3   Descriptive vs Inferential Statistics

An article in the Los Angeles Times (6/7/81) reported that "Statistics show most individuals make up their minds regarding drug use between the ages of 13 and 17."

This statement is actually a descriptive statistic statement since "statistics" refer, by definition, to numerical summary statements derived from samples.

In the sample studied, the group of subjects in the age category 13 through 17 had the highest number (or percent) declaring they had made up their mind regarding drug use.

In order to make the inference: "Most individuals. . . .13 through 17" sample data would be analyzed to determine if the obtained result could have been due to chance. In other words, we would use inferential statistics to determine the probability of the obtained result.

Multiple-Choice Items

1. A variable is: a) a value that does not change from measurement to measurement; b) a phenomenon that may take on different values; c) a sub-set of a population; d) the true value of a population in some measured characteristic.

2. A complete head count of all voters in a municipal election revealed that candidate A received 62 percent of all ballots cast. The 62 percent represents: a) a parameter; b) a statistic; c) a sample; d) a population.

3. A television rating service reported that a particular program attracted an audience of 53,000,000 people. The statement is: a) an inference; b) a parameter; c) a statistic; d) a population.

4. In a survey of 500 randomly selected coffee users, it was found that 46 percent preferred Brand A over Brand B. This value, 46 percent, represents: a) a parameter; b) an inference; c) a sample; d) a statistic.

5. Identify the qualitative variable in the following: a) amount of pressure required to fracture a casting; b) the time before a light bulb burns out; c) candidate for political office; d) the weight of packaged cereals.

6. Which of the following is a multinominal variable: a) the gender of corporation executives; b) industry-wide employment and unemployment; c) the amount of water withdrawn to irrigate crops along the Colorado River; d) types of occupations.

7. Variables whose values come as a result of measuring as opposed to counting are: a) qualitative; b) dichotomous; c) quantitative; d) multinominal.

8. The time required to complete an industrial process is: a) a continuous quantitative variable; b) a discrete quantitative variable; c) a continuous qualitative variable; d) a multinominal variable.

2

9. When we use the statistics based on samples to make statements about populations, our focus is on: a) descriptive statistics; b) inferential statistics; c) population constants; d) sample statistics.

10. Each component in a sample of 100 resistors with a nominal rating of 1,000 ohms is tested. The measurement of each resistor constitutes: a) the population; b) the parameter; c) the sample statistics; d) data.

Answers: 1. b; 2. a; 3. a; 4. d; 5. c; 6. d; 7. c; 8. a; 9. b; 10. d.

Exercises

1. A study of 155 women directors at 441 major corporations conducted by the Texas School of Management reported that nearly half the women lacked business backgrounds and usually joined an expanded board.

   (a) What is the population?

   Answer The population consists of all women directors at all major corporations.

   (b) What is the sample?

   Answer The 155 women directors at the 441 corporations represents the sample.

   (c) What is a good estimate of the population proportion of women directors who lack business backgrounds? What assumption must be made to answer this question? Identify the parameter and the statistic.

   Answer A good estimate of the population proportion (the parameter) would be "nearly half" (the obtained statistic). In order to make this estimate we must assume that the sample selected mirrors the population we are studying.

2. The Wall Street Journal reported that, in a survey of companies operating sales fleets, about 97 percent of the surveyed companies have switched to four and six cyclinder cars.

   (a) What is the population?

   (b) Based on the sample, what percentage of the population do you think has switched to four and six cylinder cars?

3. A Scholastic Magazine survey reported that of 3,000 teenage students taking home economics courses, only 36 percent plan to marry within five years.

   (a) What is the population?

   (b) What is the sample?

   (c) Identify the following:

   The variable

   data

   statistic

   descriptive statistics

   parameter

   inferential statistics

4. The Wall Street Journal reported that status, security and salary govern job choices of top MBA graduates. This conclusion came from a study of 22 of the better students at four top MBA schools.

    (a) What is the population?

    (b) What is the sample?

    (c) What is the conclusion?

Answers:

2.   (a) All companies that operate sales fleets.

    (b) Assuming that the sample of companies surveyed mirrors the population, we conclude that about 97 percent of all companies operating sales fleets are using four and six cylinder cars.

(Using a measure derived from a sample (statistic) to estimate the measure for the population (parameter) is known as "point estimation." This topic is covered more thoroughly in Chapter 7.)

3.   (a) All teenage students who take home economics courses.

    (b) The 3,000 students surveyed constitutes the sample.

    (c) The *variable* is whether or not the student plans to marry within five years.

        The *data* consist of the number of students who responded "yes."

        The *statistic* is the percentage in the sample (36 percent) who responded "yes." *Descriptive statistics* are summary statements based on the sample data.

        The *parameter* is the true percentage of students in the population who plan to marry with five years. We use *inferential statistics* to estimate this parameter.

4.   (a) The *population* consists of all the top MBA graduates.

    (b) The *sample* consists of the 22 students that were interviewed.

    (c) The conclusion is an inference about the population based on the results obtained in the sample.

Chapter 2

Organizing Statistical Data

Lesson 2-1 Frequency Tables and Frequency Distributions

When we are dealing with qualitative variables, the question does not arise concerning the number of classes to use when constructing a frequency table. If there are five qualitative categories we use five classes. Note that, by definition, the classes are mutually exclusive (an event or object cannot be in two different classes simultaneously). Some of the classes may be unordered qualitative variables and some may be ordered. To illustrate, army rank is an ordered qualitative variable. If you are an officer, as a second lieutenant you are lower than a first lieutenant in the military hierarchy. A first lieutenant is, in turn, lower than a captain, etc. When preparing graphs of ordered qualitative variables, the natural order of classes should be used. Thus, a chart showing the number of officers of various ranks should have second lieutenant at one end and five star general at the other.

For nonordered qualitative variables, there is no underlying order of the categories. Therefore, there is no single correct way to order them when preparing a chart. For example, if the qualitative variable consists of color (color of car, color of soap, color of packaged cereal, etc.), there is no natural ordering of these categories. Under these circumstances, we prefer to arrange them alphabetically.

When arranging continuous quantitative variables into classes (an operation sometimes referred to as "discretizing" the variable), the decision must be made concerning the number of classes to use. Some statisticians prefer to apply Sturgess' rule since it removes subjective factors from the decision-making process. Others find the rule too restrictive and prefer to use their own judgment, backed on past experiences and rational considerations. In most cases, however, the two procedures will yield similar decisions.

To illustrate, in Exercise 2.4 we used 8 classes for the data on drill wear. How many classes would be used under the Sturgess rule?

$$k = 1 + 3.3 \log n$$
$$= 1 + 3.3 \log 126$$
$$= 1 + (3.3)(2.1004)$$
$$= 7.93$$

This rounds to 8.

Referring to Exercise 2.6, how many classes should be used for Division A under the Sturgess rule?

$$k = 1 + 3.3 \log 97$$
$$= 1 + (3.3)(1.9868)$$
$$= 7.57$$

This rounds to 8. We used 7, a disparity of 1.

Of course, if we are using a polygon to compare distributions, both distributions should have the same class limits. Thus, Division B is shown in 8 classes even though n = 51. If we had used Sturgess' rule, and were not interested in comparing A and B, the number of classes in Division B would be:

$$k = 1 + (3.3)(1.7076)$$
$$= 6.64$$
This rounds to 7.

Lesson 2-2 Relative Frequency and Probability

When you construct a relative frequency distribution based on sample data, you have described the proportion or percentage of cases occurring within each class. For that sample, the proportions may be considered probabilities that a single draw will yield value within the limits of a given class. For example, suppose we have the following relative frequency distribution:

Class	f	Proportion
5 —under 16	5	0.0610
16—under 27	8	0.0976
27—under 38	16	0.1951
38—under 49	25	0.3049
49—under 60	19	0.2317
60—under 71	6	0.0732
71—under 82	3	0.0366
	82	1.0001 *

(*slight disparity due to rounding)

a. What is the probability of selecting a value equal to or above 27 but under 38?

b. What is the probability of selecting a value equal to or greater than 71 but less than 82?

Answers: a. 0.1951; b. 0.0366. Rounding, the chances are about 1 in 5 that you will select a value from 27 to under 38 but only about 4 in 100 that the value will be from 71 under 82. Note that, if the sample is randomly selected from the population, these probabilities provide estimates of the corresponding population probabilities.

The important topics of probability, sampling, and estimation are taken up in chapters 4, 6, and 7 respectively.

Multiple-Choice Items

1. When you arrange values of a variable in either ascending or descending orders, you have arranged them in a form of a) a frequency distribution; b) a relative frequency distribution; c) a frequency histogram; d) an array.

2. Most data in selected business fields can be accommodated by how many classes: a) 5 to 20; b) 10 to 15; c) 10 to 30; d) 8 to 14.

3. If classes do not overlap, they are: a) exhaustive; b) mutually exclusive; c) finite; d) none of the above.

4. If we divided the number of observations in a class by n, we obtain: a) a cumulative frequency; b) the relative frequency in that class; c) a relative frequency histogram; d) a frequency distribution.

5. A bar chart used with quantitative variables is called: a) a frequency polygram; b) a cumulative frequency distribution; c) an ogive; d) a histogram.

6. A distribution showing the number of observations that fall below various points in a distribution is called: a) a cumulative frequency distribution; b) a frequency polygram; c) a relative frequency polygon; d) a histogram.

7. The midpoint of the class 15 to under 30 is: a) 45; b) 22.5; c) 23; d) 22.

8. The midpoint of the class 12.25 to under 14.65 is: a) 13; b) 14.25; c) 13.45; d) 26.90.

9. When comparing frequency distributions, which type of graph is preferable? a) frequency polygons; b) histogram; c) bar graph; d) cumulative frequency curve.

10. A cumulative frequency of 58 means that 58 values of the variable: a) fall below the midpoint of the interval; b) fall below the upper limit of the interval; c) fall above the midpoint of the interval; d) fall above the upper limit of the interval.

Items 11-15 are based on the following table:

Class	f	Proportion	Cumulative	Cumulative %
0—under 5	0	0.0000	0	
5—under 10	4	0.0333	4	3.33
10—under 15	12	0.1000	16	13.33
15—under 20	16	0.1333	32	26.67
20—under 25	20	0.1667	52	43.43
25—under 30	30	0.2500	82	68.33
30—under 35	19	0.1583	101	84.17
35—under 40	13	0.1083	114	95.00
40—under 45	6	0.0500	120	100.00
		0.9999		

11. The frequency (f) 20 in the class 20— under 25 means: a) cumulatively, 20 values fall below 25; b) 20 values are distributed throughout the class; c) 20 values are above 25; d) 20 values are at the lower limit of the class.

12. The cumulative percent of 68.33 means that: a) 68.33 percent of the values are in the class 25—under 30; b) 68.33 percent of the values are 30 and above; c) 68.33 percent of the values fall below 25; d) 68.33 percent of the values fall below 30.

13. The cum f of 114 means that: a) 114 values fall under 40; b) 114 values are in the class 35—under 40; c) 114 values are above 40; d) 114 values are 35 and above.

14. The class in which 0.1333 of the values fall is: a) 10— under 15; b) 35— under 40; c) 15— under 20; d) 5—under 10.

15. The value corresponding to a cumulative percent of 26.67 is: a) 15; b) 20; c) 10; d) 16.

Answers: 1. d; 2. a; 3. b; 4. b; 5. d; 6. a; 7. b; 8. c; 9. a; 10. b; 11. b; 12. d; 13. a; 14. c; 15. b

Exercises

1. The following data show the amount of time (in minutes) 35 randomly selected customers waited in line before being helped at a regional post office:

17	24	12	69	24
7	13	18	51	41
38	6	60	14	2
16	19	12	17	31
10	19	16	21	17
11	48	14	8	22
14	4	31	18	54

(a) Set up a frequency distribution, using approximately 7 classes.

Answer: In order to find the width of the classes, we find the highest and lowest values in the data:

$$\text{approximate width} = \frac{\text{highest value - lowest value}}{\text{number of classes desired}}$$

$$= \frac{69 - 2}{7}$$

$$= 9.57$$

7

Let us round up and use 10 as the width:

Class limits	Tally	Frequency
0—under 10	✝✝✝✝	5
10—under 20	✝✝✝✝ ✝✝✝✝ ✝✝✝✝ //	17
20—under 30	////	4
30—under 40	///	3
40—under 50	//	2
50—under 60	//	2
60—under 70	//	2
		n = 35

(b) Set up a relative frequency distribution for the above data.

Answer: To find the relative frequency for each class, we divide the frequency in that class by the total number of observations (n).

Class Limits	Frequency	Relative Frequency		
0—under 10	5	5/35	=	0.1429
10—under 20	17	17/35	=	0.4857
20—under 30	4	4/35	=	0.1143
30—under 40	3	3/35	=	0.0857
40—under 50	2	2/35	=	0.0571
50—under 60	2	2/35	=	0.0571
60—under 70	2	2/35	=	0.0571
				0.9999*

(*Slight disparity due to rounding error.)

(c) Construct a histogram for the above data.

Answer: The X or horizontal axis represents the classes (we indicate each class by its lower limit) and the Y or vertical axis corresponds to the frequency within that class.

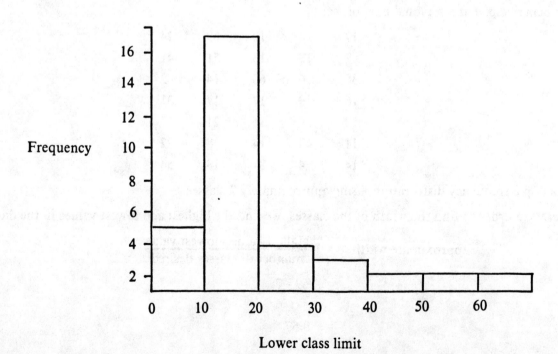

8

(d) Set up a cumulative frequency distribution for the above data.

Answer: The cumulative frequency for each class indicates the number of cases that fall below the lower limit of the succeeding class (or the upper limit of the class of interest).

Class Limits	f	Cumulative Frequency (cf)
0—under 10	5	5
10—under 20	17	5 + 17 = 22
20—under 30	4	22 + 4 = 26
30—under 40	3	26 + 3 = 29
40—under 50	2	29 + 2 = 31
50—under 60	2	31 + 2 = 33
60—under 70	2	33 + 2 = 35

(e) How many people waited less than 30 minutes?

Answer: We see, from the cumulative frequency column, that 26 people waited less than 30 minutes.

2. The personnel director at Garden State Hospital keeps records of the number of work hours lost during the course of the year by employees leaving early, taking extended lunch hours, etc. Following is the number of work hours lost by 30 randomly selected employees.

27	8	37	9	74
34	56	24	12	18
18	12	18	10	33
6	19	27	44	24
49	8	33	21	64
32	29	16	38	3

Set up a:

(a) frequency distribution, using 3—under 15 as the lowest class limits.

(b) relative frequency distribution.

(c) cumulative frequency distribution

(d) How many employees lost less than 27 work hours during the course of one year?

(e) Construct a histogram for these data.

3. M.L.P., a real estate company, sold 13 houses at the following sales prices (in dollars):

124,000	60,000
270,000	102,000
86,000	93,000
44,000	74,000
312,000	168,000
225,000	265,000
52,000	

(a) Using a width of 60, set up a frequency and relative frequency distribution.

(b) Set up a cumulative frequency and a relative cumulative frequency distribution.

(c) What percentage of the houses sold for less than $160,000?

(d) What percentage sold for more than $220,000?

4. The following table presents the percent of total sales of merchandise line sales of retail establishments in the United States in 1972.

	% Total Sales
Groceries, other foods	19.6
Meals, snacks	6.7
Alcoholic drinks	1.7
Packaged alcoholic beverages	2.6
Cigars, cigarettes, tobacco	1.4
Drugs and other health aids	2.5
Toiletries	1.0
Men's, boys' clothing, except footwear	3.4
Women's, girls' clothing, except footwear	5.9
Footwear except infants and toddlers	1.7
Curtains, draperies, dry goods	1.9
Major household appliances	1.7
Radios, TVs, musical instruments	1.9
Furniture, sleep equipment	2.3
Floor coverings	0.9
Kitchenware, home furnishings	1.4
Jewelry, optical goods	1.1
Sporting, recreational equipment	1.6
Hardware, tools, electrical supplies	1.0
Lawn and garden supplies	0.9
Lumber and building materials	3.6
Automobiles, trucks	15.1
Automotive fuels and lubricants	6.2
Auto tires, batteries, accessories	3.7
Household fuels, ice	0.9
Other merchandise	4.9
Nonmerchandise receipts	4.4

Construct a bar chart to illustrate this distribution.

Answers

2.

Class Limits	Frequency	(a) f	(b) Relative Frequency	(c) cf
3—under 15	╫╫╫ ///	8	0.2667	8
15—under 27	╫╫╫ ///	8	0.2667	16
27—under 39	╫╫╫ ////	9	0.3000	25
39—under 51	//	2	0.0667	27
51—under 63	/	1	0.0333	28
63—under 75	//	2	0.0667	30
		n = 30	1.0001 *	

(*slight disparity due to rounding)

(d)   16 employees

(e)

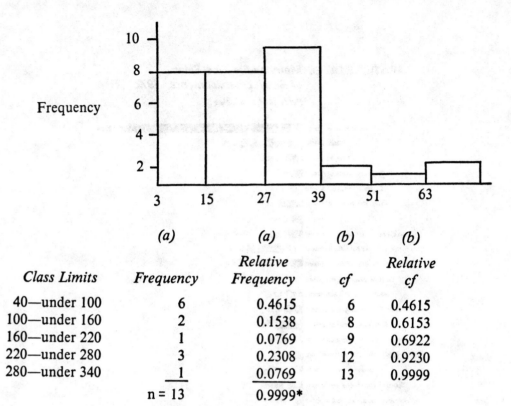

3

	(a)	*(a)* Relative	*(b)*	*(b)* Relative
Class Limits	*Frequency*	*Frequency*	*cf*	*cf*
40—under 100	6	0.4615	6	0.4615
100—under 160	2	0.1538	8	0.6153
160—under 220	1	0.0769	9	0.6922
220—under 280	3	0.2308	12	0.9230
280—under 340	1	0.0769	13	0.9999
	n = 13	0.9999*		

(*Slight disparity due to rounding.)

(c)   61 percent

(d)   31 percent

11

4

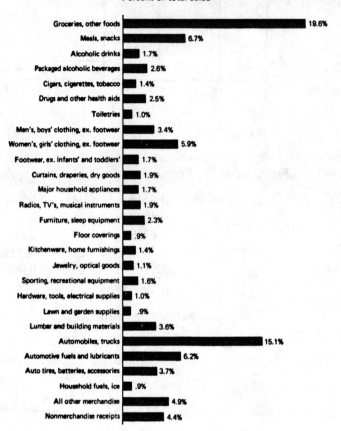

UNITED STATES *Merchandise Line Sales*
of Retail Establishments: 1972

Percent of total sales

Groceries, other foods	19.6%
Meals, snacks	6.7%
Alcoholic drinks	1.7%
Packaged alcoholic beverages	2.6%
Cigars, cigarettes, tobacco	1.4%
Drugs and other health aids	2.5%
Toiletries	1.0%
Men's, boys' clothing, ex. footwear	3.4%
Women's, girls' clothing, ex. footwear	5.9%
Footwear, ex. infants' and toddlers'	1.7%
Curtains, draperies, dry goods	1.9%
Major household appliances	1.7%
Radios, TV's, musical instruments	1.9%
Furniture, sleep equipment	2.3%
Floor coverings	.9%
Kitchenware, home furnishings	1.4%
Jewelry, optical goods	1.1%
Sporting, recreational equipment	1.6%
Hardware, tools, electrical supplies	1.0%
Lawn and garden supplies	.9%
Lumber and building materials	3.6%
Automobiles, trucks	15.1%
Automotive fuels and lubricants	6.2%
Auto tires, batteries, accessories	3.7%
Household fuels, ice	.9%
All other merchandise	4.9%
Nonmerchandise receipts	4.4%

"Twenty years ago today? Of course I know what happened! The prime rate went to 6½ percent!"

Lesson 3-1 Measures of Central Tendency

There are actually many more measures of central tendency than the mean, median, and mode. There are also the mid-range, the mid-quartile, the harmonic mean, and the geometric mean. We'll take a brief look at each of these and special situations to which they might apply.

Mid-range—When your newspaper reports the mean temperature for the day, it is actually reporting the mid-range. It is obtained simply by adding together the highest and lowest observed values of the variable of interest and dividing by 2. Thus, if the high temperature is 92° and the low is 78°, the mid-range is $\frac{92° + 78°}{2}$

= 95°. The mid-range is useful as an approximation to the arithmetic mean. If the distribution is roughly symmetrical, the approximation may be quite close. In any event, the mid-range provides a quick ballpark estimate of the arithmetic mean. If our calculated mean departs considerably from the mid-range, we should be alerted to the possibility that we have made a calculation error.

Mid-quartile—This is simply the value midway between the 25th and 75th percentiles. It may be obtained by adding together the value of the variable at each of these percentiles and dividing by 2. The mid-quartile is preferred over the crude-range for some applications because of its greater stability. That is, it is not as subject to the wide fluctuations that frequently assail the two most extreme values of the variable.

Geometric Mean—There are times when quantities are changing over time and we wish to describe an average rate of growth. The geometric mean (GM) is ideal for describing that rate of growth. To illustrate, imagine you deposited $150 in an account for three years. The rates of interest are as follows: year 1, 0.0525; year 2, 0.070; and year 3, 0.095. The calculation of the compound interest is shown in the table below:

Year	Interest Rate	Growth Factor (X)	Saving at End of Year
1	0.0525	1.0525	157.875
2	0.0700	1.0700	168.92625
3	0.0950	1.0950	184.97 (rounded)

The arithmetic mean interest rate is: (0.00525 + 0.0700 + 0.0950) ÷ 3 = 0.0725. If we were to calculate the three year interest, using 0.0725 as our average, we would obtain $150 x 1.0725 x 1.0725 x 1.0725 = 185.05. Note there there is a slight discrepancy. Over a greater number of years, the discrepancy would become larger.

The GM is defined as:

$$GM = \sqrt[n]{X_1 \times X_2 \times X_3 \times \ldots X_n}$$

In which n is the number of different values of X

In the present problem:

$$GM = \sqrt[3]{1.0525 \times 0.0700 \times 1.0950}$$
$$= 1.07236$$

Note that:

150 x 1.0723 x 1.0723 x 1.0723 = 184.97

Thus, in contrast to the arithmetic mean, the geometric mean yields the correct amount of principal plus interest.

If you have a calculator that includes the keys INV and y^x, the nth root is easily obtained. Consult the manual accompanying your calculator for specific instructions.

The *Harmonic Mean*—The harmonic mean provides an alternative method of calculating the weighted mean under a very specific set of circumstances, namely when the numerator of the ratio is constant but the denominator varies. To illustrate, suppose that you have four looms operating 12 hours a day. Each produces a different number of carpets during the period. We wish to learn the average number of minutes to manufacture each carpet. To determine the average number of minutes per carpet, the numerator is a constant (720 minutes) and the denominator varies from carpet to carpet. This is illustrated in the table below.

Loom	Number of Carpets	Number of Minutes per Carpet (X)	1/X
A	25	28.8	0.03472
B	20	36.0	0.02778
C	15	48.0	0.02083
D	18	40.0	0.02500
	78		0.10833

The harmonic mean (H) is n divided by the sum of the reciprocals of the number of minutes per carpet. Thus,

$$H = \frac{n}{\sum\limits_{i=1}^{n}\left(\frac{1}{X}\right)}$$

In the above example,

$$H = \frac{4}{0.10833} = 36.92$$

Using the weighted mean formula, verify that this answer is the same as the weighted mean.

$$\overline{X}_w = \frac{(25)(28.8)+(20)(36)+(15)(48)+(18)(40)}{25 + 20 + 15 + 18} = \frac{2880}{78} = 36.92.$$

Lesson 3-2   Calculating a Percentile

The value of the variable corresponding to a given percentile can be obtained by a slight modification of the formula for the median. This is due to the fact that the median is a special case of a percentile, namely the 50th percentile. To illustrate, the error corresponding to the 10th percentile on the Montana Rincon error data (see Table 3.4) can be obtained from the following formula:

$$\text{Percentile} = \frac{\frac{pn}{100} - F}{f} i + Lm$$

where

p = the percentile of interest

n = number of observations in the sample

F = cumulative frequency of class immediately preceding the percentile class.

f = frequency of the percentile class

i = width of the percentile class

Lm = lower limit of the percentile class

14

The 10th percentile in Rincon's data is:

$$\text{10th Percentile} = \frac{\dfrac{(10)(60)}{100} - 3}{9}(4) + (5)$$

$$= \frac{6-3}{9}(4) + 5$$

$$= 1.33 + 5 = 6.33$$

Lesson 3-3   *The Standard Deviation, Bias, and Pocket Calculators*

If you look at various books on statistics, you will note that the formulas for calculating the standard deviation and variance often differ. For example, some show:

A. $s^2 = \dfrac{\Sigma(X-\bar{X})^2}{n-1}$ and $s = \sqrt{\dfrac{\Sigma(X-\bar{X})^2}{n-1}}$

others show

B. $s^2 = \dfrac{\Sigma(X-\bar{X})^2}{n}$ and $s = \sqrt{\dfrac{\Sigma(X-\bar{X})^2}{n}}$

The formula for the variance in A is known as the unbiased estimator of the population variance. It is used in inferential statistics as an estimator of the population variance (σ^2). It is called unbiased because the mean of the sample variances of an extremely large number of random samples will yield, on the average, the value of the parameter (i.e., σ^2).

The second variance and standard deviations (B) are known as sample variance and sample standard deviation, respectively. This variance is not used as an estimator of the population σ since, on the average, it will not yield the population variance as the mean of a large number of random samples.

It is therefore, called a biased estimator.

Strictly speaking, if the sample size is small, formula B should be used whenever we wish to describe the sample variance or standard deviation and A should be used when we wish to estimate the corresponding parameters. However, in most business applications, the sample size is larger than 30. Under these circumstances, there will be a negligible difference between the variances and standard deviations calculated from the two sets of formulas. For this reason, we use n-1 in the denominator throughout the text.

If you have a statistical calculator that automatically calculates the variance and standard deviations, you must be careful to check the formula used by the calculator. Some provide s^2 and s with both n and n-1 used in the denominator. To obtain answers in agreement with those in the text, you should use the one with n-1 in the denominator. Others use n-1. This should yield results identical with ours, excepting for occasional small rounding errors. However, if n is used in the denomination, you can obtain results in agreement with ours by using the multiplier $\dfrac{n}{n-1}$. Thus,

$$s^2 = s^2\left(\frac{n}{n-1}\right) \quad \text{and} \quad s = \sqrt{s^2\left(\frac{n}{n-1}\right)}$$

15

Multiple-Choice Items

1. Given that packages sent by a mail order house have a mean weight of 12 ounces, a median of 10, and a mode of 11, if a new packaging material reduces the weight of each package by 2 ounces, the mean weight would then be: a) 10 ounces; b) 14 ounces; c) 12 ounces; d) insufficient information to answer.

2. Referring to item 1, the new median would be: a) 10 ounces; b) 8 ounces; c) 12 ounces; d) insufficient information to answer.

3. Referring to item 1, the distribution of weights is: a) normal; b) positively skewed; c) negative skewed; d) insufficient information to answer.

4. ΣX equals: a) $(X_1+\bar{X})+\ldots+(X_n\bar{X})$; b) N; c) $n\bar{X}$; d) $X_1 + X_2 + \ldots + X_n$.

5. $\dfrac{\Sigma(X-\bar{X})^2}{n-1}$ equals: a) the population standard deviation; b) the sum of squares; c) the sample variance; d) the population variance.

6. If $\Sigma(X-\bar{X})^2$ equals zero: a) all the values of the variables in the sample are identical; b) there is infinite variability; c) the sample mean equals zero; d) none of the above.

7. When an odd number of values of the variable is arranged in an array, the median is: a) the middle value; b) the mean of the two middle values; c) equal to the mean; d) the value with the greatest associated frequency.

8. The mean weight of 20 packages was 70 ounces. The mean weight of another 30 packages was 80 ounces. The mean of the 50 packages was: a) 74; b) 30; c) 75; d) 76 ounces.

9. When an even number of values of the variable is arranged in an array, the median is: a) the middle value; b) the mean of the two middle values; c) the mean of the highest and lowest values; d) the mean of the distribution.

10. In what type of distribution might the mean be at the 40th percentile? a) normal; b) positively skewed; c) negatively skewed; d) symmetrical but not normal.

11. Which statistic does not belong? a) range; b) mean; c) standard deviation; d) variance.

12. $(\Sigma X)^2$ equals: a) $X_1+X_2^2 +\ldots+X^n_2$; b) ΣX^2; c) $N\Sigma X^2$; d) none of the above.

13. Which of the following exhibits most variability? a) 6, 6, 10, 14, 14; b) 6, 8, 10, 12, 14; c) 6, 9, 10, 11, 14; d) 6, 10, 10, 10, 14.

14. Referring to item 13, which exhibits least variability? a); b); c); d).

Items 15-18 refer to the following information, the mean bulb life of 100-watt bulbs is 1,030 hours and the standard deviation is 100.

15. If a new process adds 50 hours to the life of each bulb, the new standard deviation would be: a) 150; b) 1,080; c) 100; d) insufficient information to answer.

16. If 25 hours were subtracted from the life of each bulb, the new standard deviation would be: a) 1,005; b) 75; c) 100; d) insufficient information to answer.

17. If the life of each bulb were doubled, the new standard deviation would be: a) 200; b) 100; c) 50; d) 2,060.

18. If the life of each bulb were halved, the new standard deviation would be: a) 515; b) 1,030; c) 200; d) 50.

19. The sum of the deviations divided by n equals: a) the mean; b) the variance; c) the range; d) none of the above.

20. What proportion of values of the variable in a normally distributed variable would be found between ± 1 standard deviation? a) 34; b) 16; c) 68; d) 95.

Answers: 1. a; 2. b; 3. b; 4, c; 5, c; 6, a; 7. a; 8. d; 9. b; 10. c; 11. b; 12. d; 13. a; 14. d; 15. c; 16. c; 17. a; 18. d; 19.d; 20. c.

1. Given the following ages of secretaries at a number of different firms, find the mean, median, and mode.

19	31	24
56	26	24
22	34	29
24	21	26

Answer

The *mean* is obtained by use of Formula 3.1

$$\bar{X} = \frac{\Sigma X}{n}$$

$$= \frac{336}{12} = 28.0$$

(Note that the mean is affected by extreme scores. If we eliminate 56 from the data:

$$\bar{X} = \frac{280}{11} = 25.45)$$

With ungrouped data, the *median* is found by pinpointing the middle value. However, since our data set contains an even number of values, the median is that point halfway between the two middle values. Since six values fall below an age of 24, and six values fall above 26, we calculate the median to be 25.

The *mode* is simply the most frequently occurring value. Since 24 occurs more often than any other value, we designate 24 as the mode.

2. Referring to the data in Exercise 1 above,

   a) What is the range of the ages?

   b) Calculate the sample variance and standard deviation.

Answer

   a) The range is simply the difference between the largest and smallest values. Thus, for these data,

$$\text{Range} = 56 - 19 = 27.$$

   b) We may find the sample variance through the use of formulas (3.5)

$$s^2 = \frac{\Sigma(X-\bar{X})^2}{n-1}$$

and (3.7) $\Sigma(X-\bar{X})^2 = \Sigma X^2 - \frac{(\Sigma X)^2}{n}.$

For the data on ages, we find

$$\Sigma X = 336 \qquad \Sigma X^2 = 10460 \qquad (\Sigma X)^2 = 112,896$$

$$\Sigma(X-\bar{X})^2 = 10460 - \frac{112,896}{12}$$

$$= 10460 - 9408$$

$$= 1052$$

Thus,

$$s^2 = \frac{1052}{11} = 95.6364$$

and

$$s = \sqrt{s^2} = \sqrt{95.6364} = 9.78$$

3. The following represents the price of a gallon of unleaded gasoline at nine randomly selected gasoline stations.

1.30	1.24	1.37
1.42	1.29	1.31
1.31	1.56	1.28

(a) Find the mean, median, and mode.

1.34, 1.29, 1.31

(b) Find the range, variance, and standard deviation.

.32, s^2 = .0093945, s = .096 9254

4. The following data show the home mortgage rates for conventional first mortgages on new home purchases for each month of 1977, 1978, and 1979.

1979	1978	1977
9.92	8.93	8.82
9.94	8.96	8.78
10.02	9.03	8.74
10.06	9.07	8.73
10.20	9.14	8.74
10.39	9.23	8.78
10.49	9.34	8.79
10.73	9.45	8.81
10.72	9.50	8.82
10.91	9.60	8.84
11.04	9.63	8.85
11.30	9.76	8.87

$\bar{x}$ = 10.48 mdn = 10.44 range = 1.38 s^2 = .2155181 s = .4642392

$\bar{x}$ = 9.30 mdn = 9.28 range = .83 s^2 = .080309 s = .283388

$\bar{x}$ = 8.80 mdn = 8.79 range = .14 s^2 = .0020818 s = .0456267

(a) Calculate the mean and median for each year.

(b) What is the range for each year?

(c) Calculate the variance and standard deviation for each year.

5. The following data show the per capita consumption of wine and beer (in gallons) from 1968 to 1977.

Year	Wine	Beer
1968	1.03	16.7
1969	1.11	17.2
1970	1.26	18.7
1971	1.43	18.6
1972	1.57	19.5
1973	1.61	19.8
1974	1.62	20.9
1975	1.70	21.6
1976	1.73	21.7
1977	1.81	22.5

$\bar{x}$ = 1.487 mdn = 1.59 range = .78 s^2 = .07269 s = .286108

$\bar{x}$ = 19.72 mdn = 19.65 range = 5.8 s^2 = 3.821777 s = 1.9549367

For each category,

(a) Determine the mean and median.

(b) Determine the range, variance, and standard deviation.

18

6. The following data present the industrials/price earnings ratios highs and lows for the years 1968 through 1978.

	Hi	Lo
1968	19.2	15.4
1969	19.0	16.0
1970	19.0	14.0
1971	19.4	16.6
1972	19.6	16.5
1973	15.1	11.6
1074	11.6	7.2
1975	12.5	9.1
1976	11.3	9.5
1977	10.3	8.7
1978	9.1	7.3

Handwritten annotations:

Hi
$\bar{X} = 15.1$
mdn = 15.1
range = 10.5
$s^2 = 17.846$
$S = 4.2244526$

LO
$\bar{X} = 11.99$
mdn = 11.6
range = 9.4
$s^2 = 14.38091$
$S = 3.792217$

For both the highs and lows,

(a) Find the mean and median.

(b) Determine the range, variance, and standard deviation.

7. In Exercise 1 of Chapter 2 of this Workbook, the frequency distribution of waiting time was presented. This distribution is shown below:

Class Limits	(f) Frequency	Class (X) Midpoint	(fX)	cf
0—under 10	5	5	25	5
10—under 20	17	15	255	22
20—under 30	4	25	100	26
30—under 40	3	35	105	29
40—under 50	2	45	90	31
50—under 60	2	55	110	33
60—under 70	2	65	130	35
	n = 35		ΣfX = 815	

(a) Calculate the mean waiting time for this sample.

Answer

To find the mean of grouped data, we use formula (3.2)

$$\bar{X} = \frac{\Sigma fX}{n}$$

$$= \frac{815}{35}$$

$$= 23.29$$

(b) Find the median waiting time.

Answer

To use formula (3.4)

$$Mdn = \left(\frac{0.5n-F}{f}\right) i + Lm$$

We must first identify the median class, or the class which contains the middle observation ($\frac{n}{2}$ or 17.5th case). The class 10—under 20 includes the 17.5th observation.

Thus, F = cumulative frequency of the class immediately preceding the median class, or 5.

$$f \quad = \text{frequency in the median class, or 17.}$$
$$Lm \quad = \text{lower limit of the median class, or 10}$$

Thus,

$$\text{Mdn} = \left(\frac{0.5(35) - 5}{17}\right) 10 + 10$$
$$= 17.35$$

(2) Find the mode.

More people waited between 10—under 20 minutes. Thus, the mode corresponds to the midpoint of that class, or 15.

(d) Calculate the sample variance and standard deviation.

The following values are needed for these calculations:

Class Limits	f	Midpoint X	X^2	fX^2
0—under 10	5	5	25	125
10—under 20	17	15	225	3,285
20—under 30	4	25	625	2,500
30—under 40	3	35	1,225	3,675
40—under 50	2	45	2,025	4,050
50—under 60	2	55	3,025	6,050
60—under 70	2	65	4,225	8,450
			$\Sigma fX^2 =$	28,675

$$\Sigma f(X-\bar{X})^2 = \Sigma fX^2 - \frac{(\Sigma fX)^2}{n}$$

$$= 28,675 - \frac{(815)^2}{35}$$

$$= 9,697.14$$

$$s^2 = \frac{\Sigma f(X-\bar{X})^2}{n-1} = \frac{9,697.14}{34}$$

$$= 285.21$$

$$s = \sqrt{285.21} = 16.89$$

(e) Using Chebyshev's theorem, estimate the range of waiting times that will include 31 percent of all delays.

Answer

Using Chebyshev's theorem, at least 31 percent of all waiting times will be between the mean and ± 1.2 standard deviations. Thus the minimum range of waiting times that will occur 31 percent of the time is:

$$\bar{X} \pm (k)(s) = 23.29 \pm (1.2)(16.89) = 3.02 \text{ to } 43.56$$

8. The personnel director or a large rehabilitation hospital randomly assigned 50 employees to a new training program. She then administered a test to these employees (Group A) and the same test to a matched group of 50 employees who did not participate in the training program (Group B). The following presents the frequency distribution of test scores obtained by each group.

20

Group A Group B
$\bar{X} = 71.8$ $\bar{X} = 70.2$
$mdn = 72.5$ $mdn = 70$
$= 165.0612252 =$
$= 12.847615$ 311.18367
$S = 17.640398$

Test Scores	f Group A	f Group B	X Group A	X Group B	fx Group A	fx Group B
40—under 50	2	9	45	45	90	405
50—under 60	8	7	55	55	440	385
60—under 70	11	9	65	65	715	585
70—under 80	16	9	75	75	1 200	675
80—under 90	9	6	85	85	765	510
90—under 100	4	10	95	95	380	950
	50	50			3590	3510

cf Group A	cf Group B
2	9
10	16
21	25
37	34
46	40
50	50

(a) Calculate the mean and median for each group.

(b) Calculate the variance and standard deviation for each group.

(c) Comment on the test performance of the two groups.

There is more variability in GroupB Test Scores.

Answers

3.

(a)
$\Sigma X = 12.08$
$\bar{X} = 1.34$
$Mdn = 1.31$
$Mode = 1.31$

(b)
$\Sigma X^2 = 16.2892$
$Range = 1.56 - 1.24$
$= 0.32$

$s^2 = \dfrac{0.0752}{8} = 0.0094$

$s = 0.0969$

4.

	ΣX	ΣX^2	(a) Mean	(a) Median	(b) Range	Variance	(c) Standard Deviation
1977	105.57	928.7749	8.7975	8.80	0.14	0.0021	0.0456
1978	111.64	1039.5074	9.3033	9.285	0.83	0.0803	0.2834
1979	125.72	1319.4972	10.4767	10.44	1.38	0.2155	0.4642

5.

	ΣX	ΣX^2	(a) Mean	(a) Median	(b) Range	(b) Variance	(b) Standard Deviation
Wine	14.87	22.7659	1.487	1.59	0.78	0.0727	0.2696
Beer	197.2	3923.18	19.72	19.65	5.8	3.8219	1.9549

6.

	ΣX	ΣX^2	(a) Mean	(a) Median	(b) Range	(b) Variance	(b) Standard Deviation
Hi	166.1	2686.57	15.1	15.1	10.5	17.846	4.2245
Lo	131.9	1725.41	11.99	11.6	9.4	14.3809	3.7922

8

	ΣfX	ΣfX^2	*(a)* $\bar{X}$	*(a)* Mdn.	*(b)* Variance	*(b)* Standard Deviation
Group A	3,590	265,850	71.8	72.5	165.0612	12.85
Group B	3,510	261,650	70.2	70.0	311.1837	17.64

(c) Although the means and medians for the two groups are fairly similar, Group B test scores show greater variability.

Lesson 4-1 When to Use the Multiplication and Addition Rules

Perhaps the most common difficulty experienced by students newly initiated to probability theory involves the decision about when to use the multiplication rule and when to use the addition rule. There are two questions you should ask yourself.

1. Are you talking about a single draw from a population or more than one draw?

2. Are you asking the probability of both events occurring simultaneously (i.e., both A and B) or the probability of either event A or B?

If you are concerned with a single draw from a population, the following table should help you decide the appropriate formula to use. But first, you should answer one further question.

3. Are the events mutually exclusive or non-mutually exclusive? Note that the multiplication rule never applies to mutually exclusive events when there is a single draw. The probability of obtaining both event A and event B is zero.

Table of Formulas for the multiplication rule when there is a single draw from the population and the event is either mutually exclusive or not mutually exclusive.

Multiplication Rule (Joint probability; both A and B)		Addition Rule (Either A or B)	
Mutually Exclusive	*Nonmutually Exclusive*	*Mutually Exclusive*	*Nonmutually Exclusive*
both a head and a tail	both a spade and a queen	either a head or a tail	either a spade or a queen
CANNOT OCCUR	$p(A \text{ and } B) = p(A)p(B)$	$p(A \text{ or } B) = p(A) + p(B) - p(A \text{ and } B)$	$p(A \text{ or } B) = p(A) + p(B) - p(A \text{ and } B)$
By definition of mutually exclusive, $P(A \text{ and } B) = 0$	$p(A \text{ and } B) = \left(\frac{13}{52}\right)\left(\frac{4}{52}\right) = \frac{1}{52}$	Since $p(A \text{ and } B) = 0$ for mutually exclusive events $p(A \text{ or } B) = p(A) + p(B)$	$p(A \text{ or } B) = \frac{13}{52} + \frac{4}{52} - \frac{1}{52} = \frac{16}{52}$

Lesson 4-2 Repeated Draws, with Replacement, from a Population Whose Structure Is Known

The reason that games of chance (e.g., cards, dice, coin tosses) figure so prominently in illustrating probability theory is that the structure of the population is known. Consequently, the demonstration of various probability calculations is conceptually "clean." To illustrate, when tossing a single die twice, there are 36 possible events. The probability of each is obtained by the multiplication rule. What is the probability of obtaining a 5 followed by a 6, in that order? Since $p(A = 5) = 1/6$ and $p(B = 6) = 1/6$, $p(A \text{ and } B) = (1/6)(1/6) = 1 \div 36$.

If we are not concerned with the order (5 before 6 versus 6 before 5), we invoke the addition rule to answer the question: what is the probability of obtaining either a 5 and a 6 or a 6 and a 5. Since each of these is 1/36, $p(5 \text{ and } 6 \text{ or } 6 \text{ and } 5) = 1/36 + 1/36 = 1/18$.

The table below shows the enumeration of all possible sequences and the associated probabilities of tossing a single die twice.

Sequence	p	Sequence	p	Sequence	p	Sequence	p	Sequence	p
1 and 1	1/36	2 and 2	1/36	3 and 3	1/36	4 and 4	1/36	5 and 5	1/36
1 and 2	1/36	2 and 3	1/36	3 and 4	1/36	4 and 5	1/36	5 and 6	1/36
2 and 1	1/36	3 and 2	1/36	4 and 3	1/36	5 and 4	1/36	6 and 5	1/36
1 and 3	1/36	2 and 4	1/36	3 and 5	1/36	4 and 6	1/36	6 and 6	1/36
3 and 1	1/36	4 and 2	1/36	5 and 3	1/36	6 and 4	1/36		
1 and 4	1/36	2 and 5	1/36	3 and 6	1/36				
4 and 1	1/36	5 and 2	1/36	6 and 3	1/36				
1 and 5	1/36	2 and 6	1/36						
5 and 1	1/36	6 and 2	1/36						
1 and 6	1/36								
6 and 1	1/36								

Note that the sum of the probabilities of all the possible sequences is 1.00.

When we have enumerated all possible sequences, we have described the sample space. We may use this sample space to answer any questions we wish concerning possible outcomes of our experiment.

What is the probability that the sum of the two tosses will equal 11?

Since 5 and 6 or 6 and 5 will satisfy this condition, p(5 and 6 or 6 and 5) = 1/36+1/36 = 1/18.

What is the probability that the sum will equal 7?

Here we find the following: 1 and 6, 6 and 1, 2 and 5, 5 and 2, 3 and 4, or 4 and 3. Since the probability of each is 1/36, the addition rule yields:

p(sum equal to 7) = 1/36+1/36+1/36+1/36+1/36+1/36
                  = 6(1/36) = 1/6.

What is the probability that the sum will equal either 4 or 10?

p(sum equal to 4 or 10) = p(1+3)+p(3+1)+p(2+2)+p(4+6)+p(6+4)+p(5+5)
                        = 1/36+1/36+1/36+1/36+1/36+1/36
                        = 6(1/36) = 1/6.

What is the probability that the sum will equal 6?

p(sum equal to 6) = p(1+5)+p(5+1)+p(2+4)+p(4+2)+p(3+3)
                  = 1/36+1/36+1/36+1/36 + 1/36
                  = 5/36

Lesson 4-2   Use of Joint Probability Table to Obtain Conditional Probabilities

In the New England Journal of Medicine (Rosebloom et al., 1981), the following results are reported among juvenile patients with more than four and a half years of diabetes. Of 169 patients, 82 had joint limitation. Forty-one of these 82 also had microvascular complications. Only 10 of 87 patients without joint limitation had microvascular complications. Based on this information, the following table of cell and marginal frequencies may be constructed.

		Joint Limitation		
		A	$\bar{\text{A}}$	
microvascular	$\bar{\text{B}}$	41	77	118
complications	B	41	10	51
		82	87	169

24

By dividing each cell and marginal frequency by n (i.e., 169), we may obtain a probability value, based on the sample, for each cell and marginal frequency. These are shown below.

	A	$\overline{A}$	
$\overline{B}$	0.24	0.46	0.70
B	0.24	0.06	0.30
	0.48	0.52	1.00

The following joint probability table provides a useful aid in understanding the calculation of conditional probabilities.

	A	$\overline{A}$	
$\overline{B}$	p(A and B)	p($\overline{A}$ and $\overline{B}$)	p($\overline{B}$)
B	p(A and $\overline{B}$)	p$\overline{A}$ and B)	p(B)
	p(A)	p($\overline{A}$)	

Thus, to find the probability of microvascular complications given that joint limitation has been observed:

$$p(B|A) = \frac{p(A \text{ and } B)}{p(A)} = \frac{0.24}{0.48} = 0.50$$

Similarly, the probability of microvascular complications given that joint limitation has not been observed:

$$p(B|\overline{A}) = \frac{p(\overline{A} \text{ and } B)}{p(\overline{A})} = \frac{0.06}{0.52} = 0.12$$

We may also calculate the probability that joint limitation will be observed given that microvascular complications have been found:

$$p(A|B) = \frac{p(A \text{ and } B)}{p(A)} = \frac{0.24}{0.30} = 0.80$$

Finally, the probability that joint limitation will be found when microvascular complications have not been observed is:

$$p(A|\overline{B}) = \frac{p(A \text{ and } \overline{B})}{p(\overline{B})} = \frac{0.24}{0.70} = 0.34$$

Source: Limited Joint Mobility in Childhood Diabetes Mellitus Indicates Increased Risk for Microvascular Disease. Rosenbloom, A. L., Silverstein, J., Lezotte, D. C., Richardson, K., and McCallum, M. *New England Journal of Medicine*, 1981, #4, pp. 191-94.

Multiple-Choice Items

1. Probabilities may vary from: a) -1 to 0; b) -1.00 to + 1.00; c) 0.00 to 1.00; d) 0.05 to 0.95.

2. When one event has no predictable effect on another, the events are: a) unreliable; b) biased; c) independent; d) exhaustive.

3. The statement, "Based on months of observation, the probability is 0.25 that a given item, selected at random from the daily output, will be defective," probably represents: a) a probability statement based on the classical approach; b) a subjective probability; c) a relative frequency probability; d) insufficient basis for knowing.

4. Salt mines of geological inactive regions are considered as possible burial sites for radioactive wastes. Which of the following is probably the most reasonable assessment of the risk? a) there is no chance that a radioactive leak will develop because the site will not become active; b) the chance of a leak is less than in humid and geologically active surroundings; c) the chance is very high that the site will become active since it is "overdue"; d) we have no means of assessing the likelihood that different sites will become active.

5. If p(A)+p($\bar{A}$) = 1.00, the two events or categories are: a) mutually exclusive and exhaustive; b) mutually exclusive and independent; c) exhaustive and independent; d) not mutually exclusive but exhaustive.

6. Empirical probabilities: a) are absolutely stable over time; b) are based on theoretical populations whose structures are know; c) may change with changed circumstances; d) are too subjective to be of practical value.

7. Mutually exclusive events are: a) always related; b) never independent; c) dependent; d) all of the above.

8. In one toss of a pair of dice, the probability that the sum will be 3 is: a) 1/36; b) 1/12; c) (1/36)^2; d) 1/18.

9. When p(B|A) = p(B), the events are: a) independent; b) nonrandom; c) not independent; d) none of the above.

10. For nonindependent events, p(A)p(B|A) equals: a) p(B); b) p(A); c) p(B)p(A|B); d) 1.00-p(B).

11. When events are mutually exclusive and dichotomous, p(A|B) equals: a) zero; b) p(B|A); c) 1-[p(A)+p(B)]; d) all of the above.

12. In a single draw, the probability of randomly selecting a spade or a 9 from a 52-card deck of playing cards is: a) 15/52; b) 1/51; c) 4/13; d) 17/51.

13. All possible outcomes in a sampling experiment is known as: a) a sample point; b) the sample space; c) an event; d) none of the above.

Exercises 14-16 are based on the following figure.

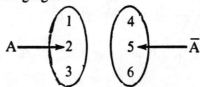

14. The sample points 1 and 4 are: a) mutually exclusive and exhaustive; b) exhaustive but not mutually exclusive; c) neither mutually exclusive nor exhaustive; d) mutually exclusive but not exhaustive.

15. Each of the values 1 through 6 is: a) an outcome; b) the sample space; c) a compound event; d) none of the above.

16. The values 1, 2, and 3, taken collectively are: a) an outcome; b) the sample space; c) an event; d) none of the above.

17. In the following diagram,

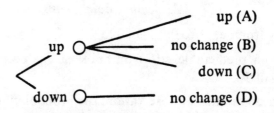

the branch showing up-no change is: a) A; b) B; c) C; d) D.

18. Independent events: a) are mutually exclusive; b) may be mutually exclusive, depending on circumstances; c) are not mutually exclusive; d) none of the above.

Items 19-22 are based on the following table. It shows the breakdown, at three different locations, of numbers of employees absent for ten or more days in a year vs. the number with fewer than ten absences.

Location	A Ten or more absences during the year	Ā Fewer than 10 absences during the year	Total
B	30	170	200
C	25	100	125
D	45	105	150
	100	375	475

19. The probability that any given employee, selected at random, will have been absent 10 or more times is: a) 0.15; b) 0.20; c) 0.30; d) 0.21.

20. The probability that any given employee, selected at random, would be from location D is: a) 0.21; b) 0.89; c) 0.32; d) none of the above.

21. The probability that any given employee, selected at random from location D, would be absent fewer than 10 times is: a) 0.45; b) 0.28; c) 0.30; d) 0.85.

22. The probability that any given employee, selected at random from location B will be absent 10 or more times is: a) 0.30; b) 0.45; c) 0.06; d) 0.15.

Answers: 1) c; 2) c; 3) c; 4) b; 5) a; 6) c; 7) d; 8) d; 9) a; 10) c; 11) d; 12) c; 13) b; 14) d; 15) a; 16) c; 17) b; 18) c; 19) d; 20) c; 21) d; 22) d.

Exercises

1. What is the probability of obtaining either a 7 (event A) or an 11 (event B) on the first toss of a pair of dice? Describe the sample points and the sample space. Are the events A and B mutually exclusive?

Answer

There are 36 sample points resulting from the toss of a pair of dice. These sample points, shown below, comprise the sample space.

1,1	2,1	3,1	4,1	5,1	6,1
1,2	2,2	3,2	4,2	5,2	6,2
1,3	2,3	3,3	4,3	5,3	6,3
1,4	2,4	3,4	4,4	5,4	6,4
1,5	2,5	3,5	4,5	5,5	6,5
1,6	2,6	3,6	4,6	5,6	6,6

The circled sample points comprise event A. Since there are six, $p(A) = \dfrac{6}{36}$

The sample points in the squares comprise event B. Since there are two, $p(B) = \dfrac{2}{36}$. The two events are mutually exclusive since they do not include common sample points. Thus:

$$p(A \text{ or } B) = \frac{6}{36} + \frac{2}{36} = \frac{8}{36} = 0.22$$

2. The owner of an automobile dealership runs spot advertisements on both radio and T.V. An independent survey of new car buyers reveals that 45 percent of those interviewed had seen at least one of the T.V. spots (event A). Of this 45 percent, 60 percent had heard him on radio. Seventy-five percent of all the people interviewed had heard the car dealer on radio (event B).

(a) What is the probability that a prospective car buyer saw the car dealer on T.V. and heard him on radio?

Answer

We are lookng for the joint probability of these two events, i.e., p(A and B). We have been given the following probabilities:

$$p(A) = 0.45$$
$$p(B) = 0.75$$
$$p(B|A) = 0.60$$

Since A and B are *not* independent, i.e., $p(B|A) \neq p(B)$ or $0.60 \neq 0.75$, we must use the multiplication rule for dependent events:

$$p(A \text{ and } B) = p(A)p(B|A) = (0.45)(0.60) = 0.27$$

(b) What is the probability that a car buyer has either seen the car dealer on T.V. or heard him on radio?

Answer

Since these events are *not* mutually exclusive (i.e., it is possible to have both seen and heard the car dealer), we use the following addition rule:

$$p(A \text{ or } B) = p(A) + p(B) - p(A \text{ and } B)$$
$$= 0.45 + 0.75 - 0.27$$
$$= 0.93$$

(c) Given that a car buyer heard the dealer on the radio, what is the probability that the buyer also saw the dealer on T.V.?

Answer

Here we are interested in the conditional probability of A given B, or p(A|B).

$$p(A|B) = \frac{p(A \text{ and } B)}{p(B)}$$

$$= \frac{0.27}{0.75}$$

$$= 0.36$$

(d) What is the probability that a car buyer did *not* see the dealer on T.V.? What is the probability that the car dealer was *not* heard on radio?

Answer

These questions refer to the complements of events A and B, i.e., $\overline{A}$ and $\overline{B}$.

$$\text{Since } p(A) = 0.45; \ p(\overline{A}) = 0.55$$
$$\text{Since } p(B) = 0.75; \ p(\overline{B}) = 0.25$$

e. The following joint probability table summarizes the probabilities we have obtained thus far. Fill in the missing values.

	yes T.V. A	no $\overline{A}$	marginal probabilities
B	0.27	.48	0.75
Radio			
$\overline{B}$	.18	.07	0.25
marginal probabilities	0.45	0.55	

Answer

Let us obtain the missing values through the use of the addition rule. For example,

$$p(A) = p(A \text{ and } B) + p(A \text{ and } \overline{B})$$

Therefore,

$$
\begin{aligned}
p(A \text{ and } \overline{B}) &= p(A) - p(A \text{ and } B) \\
&= 0.45 - 0.27 \\
&= 0.18
\end{aligned}
$$

$$
\begin{aligned}
p(\overline{A} \text{ and } B) &= p(B) - p(A \text{ and } B) \\
&= 0.75 - 0.27 \\
&= 0.48
\end{aligned}
$$

$$
\begin{aligned}
p(\overline{A} \text{ and } \overline{B}) &= p(\overline{A}) - p(\overline{A} \text{ and } B) \\
&= 0.55 - 0.48 \\
&= 0.07
\end{aligned}
$$

Thus, the completed joint probability table:

		T.V. A	$\overline{A}$	marginal p
Radio	B	0.27	0.48	0.75
	$\overline{B}$	0.18	0.07	0.25
marginal p		0.45	0.55	

(f) Given that a car buyer did *not* hear the dealer on radio, what is the probability that the buyer saw him on T.V.?

Answer

Once again we are interested in a conditional probability:

$$
\begin{aligned}
P(A|\overline{B}) &= \frac{p(A \text{ and } \overline{B})}{p(\overline{B})} \\
&= \frac{0.18}{0.75} \\
&= 0.24
\end{aligned}
$$

(g) Given that the car dealer was *not* seen on T.V., what is the probability he was also missed on radio?

Answer   Symbolically we are asking:

$$p(\overline{B}|\overline{A}) = \frac{p(\overline{A} \text{ and } \overline{B})}{p(\overline{A})}$$

$$= \frac{0.07}{0.55}$$

$$= 0.13$$

(h) Given that the car dealer was *not* heard on radio, what is the probability he was also missed on T.V.?

Answer

In this case, we are asking:

$$p(\overline{A}|\overline{B}) = \frac{p(\overline{A} \text{ and } \overline{B})}{p(\overline{B})}$$

$$= \frac{0.07}{0.25}$$

$$= 0.28$$

3. An agricultural combine has determined that a yield of fifty bushels an acre of a given crop is necessary to make a satisfactory profit. It is considering the acquisition of two low-land properties, one with high and one with low moisture content in the soil; and two high-land properties, also with either high or low moisture content in the soil. Given the following joint probability table:

	High moisture B_1	Low moisture B_2
Low-land A_1	0.35	0.30
High-land A_2	0.25	0.10

Find:

a) $p(A_1)$; b) $p(A_2)$; c) $p(B_1)$; d. $p(B_2)$ e) $p(A_1|B_1)$; f) $p(A_1|B_2)$; g) $p(A_2|B_1)$; h) $p(A_2|B_2)$.

Verbalize each of the probabilities in a) through h).

4. Refer back to Exercise 2.5 in the text, what approach to probability is being used?

Answers

3. a) $p(A_1)$ = probability that the property is low-land.
        = 0.65

    b) $p(A_2)$ = probability that the property is high-land.
        = 0.35

    c) $p(B_1)$ = probability that land has a high moisture content.
        = 0.60

    d) $p(B_2)$ = probability that land has a low moisture content.
        = 0.40

    e) $p(A_1|B_1)$ = Given that the land has a high moisture content, the probability that it is low-land.
        $= \frac{0.35}{0.60} = 0.58$

f) $p(A_1|B_2)$ = Given that the land has a low moisture content, the probability that it is low-land.

$\quad = \dfrac{0.30}{0.40} = 0.75$

g) $p(A_2|B_1)$ = Given that the land has a high moisture content, the probability that it is high-land.

$\quad = \dfrac{0.25}{0.60} = 0.42$

h) $p(A_2|B_2)$ = Given that the land has a low moisture content, the probability that it is high-land.

$\quad = \dfrac{0.10}{0.40} = 0.25$

4. Empirical.

Chapter 5

Random Variables and Probability Distributions

Lesson 5-1 The Expectation of a Discrete Random Variable and Games of Chance

In the text we pointed out that the origins of the concept of expected value is tied to games of chance. The use of expected value in this context can easily be demonstrated by a simple example involving a lottery. Imagine that 200,000 tickets are sold at a price of $2 a ticket. Ten prizes are going to be awarded: $100,000; $50,000; 3 prizes of $25,000; 4 prizes of $10,000; 3 prizes of $5,000; and 10 prizes of $1,000. Although we are sampling without replacement, the number of tickets is so large that we will assume that the probability of a winning ticket being selected in each drum is 0.000005.

Amount Win	f	$p(X)$	$Xp(X)$
99,998	1	0.000005	0.499990
49,998	1	0.000005	0.249990
24,998	3	0.000015	0.374970
9,998	4	0.000020	0.199960
4,998	3	0.000015	0.074970
998	10	0.000050	0.049900
-2	199,978	0.999890	-1.999780
	200,000	1.000000	$E(X) = -0.55$

What we see is that the expected gain is minus 55 cents. This means that, if you purchased tickets for the lottery over and over again, you would expect your long-term loss to be 55 cents per ticket. Note that, in terms of monetary value, it is not a wise economic decision to purchase a lottery ticket. However, other values frequently come into play. Some players would say that it is well worth the risk of 55 cents for the "excitement of the chase."

What would a fair game be? A fair game is one in which $E(X) = 0$. That is, there would be no long-term gain nor long-term loss. This would happen whenever the amount lost is equal to the amount gained. Of course, the entrepreneurs promoting the lottery could not stay in business very long if they also promoted a fair game.

Lesson 5-2 The Binomial and Assumption of Independence

The assumption that successes are independent is crucial in evaluating the likelihood of many system failures. To illustrate, imagine that a stage in a nuclear reactor is so critical that failure would lead to devastating results. As a safety measure, the primary system is backed up by two presumably independent fall-back systems. If the primary system fails, the secondary system takes over. If both the primary and the secondary system fail, the tertiary system comes into play. It has been estimated that the probability of a given system failing is 0.0001. On the assumption that the probability of failures of the primary and two back-up systems are independent, we would calculate the probability of a system failure as Q^3 (that is, all three fail). In this example, $Q^3 = (0.0001)^3 = 1^{-12}$. The probability of a simultaneous failure of all three would appear to be remote. But what if the probabilities of failure are not independent? This could happen if the failure of the primary system puts an exceptional burden on the secondary system, increasing its likelihood of failure. This would appear remote if the back-up system is called into play only when the primary system fails and its capabilities are equal to those of the primary system. It would be less remote if the back-up system operates concurrently with the primary system. For example, failure of one engine in an airplane could put sufficient extra load on another engine so that it's likehood of failure is increased.

There are other circumstances that would cause the system to be nonindependent. Returning to the nuclear generator site, what if the plant is built in a geologically active area? If the failure of the primary system results from a massive earthquake, it is possible and quite probable that the back-up systems would fail for the same reasons.

Lesson 5-3   Expected Value of a Binomial Variable

In *How Numbers Lie* (Runyon, 1981) the author describes one of the earliest reported scams perpetrated by the two Maiar brothers. The setting is 16th Century Antwerp. The brothers agreed to pay a pregnant woman 30 livres if a girl was born but to receive payment of 48 livres following the birth of a boy. Assuming that the probability of each is 0.50 (which it is not in the present day United States; the probability of a boy being born to white parents has averaged 0.5141 over the past decade; to black parents, the proportion is 0.5069), the expected gain on a transaction is:

Event	Gain(X)	p(X)	Xp(X)
boy	48	.50	24
girl	-30	.50	-15
			E(X) = 9

In three transactions, the expected gain is:

Event	Gain (X)	p(X)	Xp(X)
3 boys	144	0.125	18.00
2 boys	66	0.375	24.75
1 boy	-12	0.375	-4.50
0 boys	-90	0.125	-11.25
			E(X) = 27

You might check that the expected gain per transaction

$$\left(\frac{E(X)}{n} = \frac{27}{3} = 9 \right)$$

remains the same no matter how many transactions are entered into. However, the greater the number of transactions consummated, the greater is the absolute value of the expected gain.

Multiple Choice Items

1. A variable is said to be _____a_____ within its range if, for a pair of real values with p > 0, there exist other values between these two for which p = 0. a) continuous; b) independent; c) discrete; d) dichotomous.

2. We cannot list all possible values, within its range, of a _____a_____ random variable: a) continuous; b) discrete; c) qualitative; d) none of the above.

3. A state is offering a lottery in which a single prize of one million dollars will be given to the winner. It expects to sell 2.5 million tickets at $1 each. The expected net gain (or loss) from purchasing a ticket is: a) +$0.50; b) -$0.50; c) +$0.60; d) -$0.60.

4. In Bernoulli trials: a) P+Q = 1.00; b) P =1.00-Q; c) Q = 1.00-P; d) all of the above.

5. If we selected five observations from a two-category population, the total number of difference sequences of success and failure is: a) 2^5; b) 5^2; c) 5!; d) 2!

6. The distribution that yields the probability of a given number of successes in n Bernoulli trials is: a) normal; b) Poisson; c) binomial; d) multinomial.

7. The value p(x) for a particular P is identical to _____a_____ for the corresponding Q: a) q(n-x); b) p(n); c) q(n); d) p(n-x).

34

8. Given: $px = \dfrac{n!}{x!(n-x)!} P^x Q^{n-x}$, $n = 5$, $x = 4$, $p = \frac{1}{2}$

   The probability of x objects in the Q category is: a) 0.15625; b) 0.03125; c) 0.0625; d) 0.25.

9. Which of the following does *not* apply to a situation in which binomial applies: a) the variable consists of two mutually exclusive and exhaustive categories; b) the probability of success varies from trial to trial; c) each trial is identical; d) our interest is in ascertaining the chance of x successes in n trials.

10. The coefficient of the binomial for three successes in the expansion $(P+Q)^4$ equals: a) 1; b) 4; c) 6; d) 5.

11. If n = 13, the probability that 4 or more failures is equal to the probability of _____ or fewer successes: a) 4; b) 9; c) 10; d) cannot answer without knowing the value of P and Q.

12. In a Poisson process, if the probability of an event occurring in Y time is 0.15, the probability that the event will occur in 3Y time is: a) 0.5; b) 0.05; c) 0.45; d) 0.33.

13. Unlike the binomial, the Poisson deals with: a) discrete events; b) an infinite number of countable points; c) a theoretical probability distribution; d) none of the above.

14. To which of the following is a Poisson process likely to apply: a) a coin tossing experiment; b) the number of people standing in line at a movie theater over a 24-hour period; c) possible poker hands in a deck of playing cards; d) the number of flaws per yard in carpets produced by a loom.

15. If $\lambda = 6$ and t = .2, $\mu =$ a) 1.2; b) 12; c) 30; d) 3.0.

16. If, on the average 48 infants are born at a hospital each 24-hour period, the mean per half-hour is _____ and λ equals _____: a) 4, 0.5; b) 2, 4; c) 0.5, 4; d) 0.5, 2.

17. The Poisson approximation to binomial probabilities is satisfactory when: a) n is small and nP is small; b) n is large and nP is small; c) n is small and nP is large; d) n is large and nP is large.

18. To which of the following does the statement apply, "We describe the probability distribution in terms of probabilities associated with intervals of values of the random variable.": a) continuous random variable; b) discrete variables; c) Bernoulli trials; d) Poisson processes.

19. If X = 20, $\mu = 30$, and $\sigma = 5$, z equals: a) 10; b) 2; c) -10; d) -2.

20. To calculate a z- score, we require: a) the value of a variable; b) the standard deviation of the distribution; c) the mean of the distribution; d) all of the above.

21. In a normally distributed variable, the percentage of the distribution exceeding a z- score of 0 is: a) 20; b) 50; c) 0; d) 100.

22. If z = 1.5, n = 30, X = 52, $\mu = 40$, σ equals: a) 0.4; b) 0.27; c) 8; d) 26.67.

Answers: 1. c; 2. a; 3. d; 4. d; 5. a; 6. c; 7. d; 8. a; 9. b; 10. b; 11. b; 12. c; 13. b; 14. d; 15. a; 16. d; 17. b; 18. a; 19. d; 20. d; 21. b; 22. c.

Exercises

1. In order to enter a particular contest, you must send an entry form with a self-addressed stamped envelope. With the current cost of postage at 18 cents, your investment, for each entry, is 36 cents. The following table presents the prizes offered and the number available at each prize level. How much might an individual "expect" to win in the long run by participating in this contest? Keeping in mind the cost of postage, is this a "winning" or "losing" situation for the contestant?

$$p(x) = \dfrac{n!}{x!(n-x)!} P^x Q^{n-x}$$

Prize Amount	# Prizes Available
$1,000	10
100	100
50	500
20	2,000
10	4,000
5	13,500
0	979,890

Answer

In order to determine the expected value, we must first find the probability distribution. We then multiply each prize amount (X) by its associated probability and sum. This sum provides a type of weighted average that the contestant would expect to win "on the average."

Prize Amount (X)	f	p (X)*	X p (X)
1,000	10	0.00001	0.0100
100	100	0.00010	0.0100
50	500	0.00050	0.0250
20	2,000	0.00200	0.0400
10	4,000	0.00400	0.0400
5	13,500	0.01350	0.0675
0	979,890	0.97989	0
	n = 1,000,000		0.1925

*Each of these values is obtained by dividing the frequency by n = 1,000,000.

Thus, since the expected value of 0.1925 is less than the cost of entering (0.36), this is a "losing" proposition.

2. From prior experience, The Registrar of Contractors has found that the probability is about 0.40 that a pool owner will submit an official complaint within one year after completion of the pool. If 20 pools are completed during a given month, what is the probability that 10 or more complaints will be filed within one year?

3. Marie has to decide between two job offers. For Job #1, the commissions earned vs the cost of sales are set up so that she needs at least two sales in six contacts where the probability is 0.30 of consummating a single sale. For Job #2, she needs at least 3 sales in 5 contacts where the probability is 0.50 of consummating a single sale. Which job offers a better probability of success?

4. During the eight hour period between 9 a.m. and 5 p.m., an airlines reservation switchboard receives, on the average 2,496 calls. The distribution of calls has been found to be uniform throughout the period. a) What is the average number of calls per minute? b) It is capable of handling a maximum of nine calls per minute. What is the probability that, during any given minute, its switchboard will be overloaded (i.e., $x > 9$)?

5. In planning for the construction of a new obstetrics facility, it is anticipated that an average of 12 infants will be born during each 24 hour period. a) What is the probability that two will be born in a one hour period? b) What is the probability that two or more will be born during that period?

6. In the three months preceding the 1980 presidential election, the number of shares traded on the New York Stock Exchange was normally distributed with a mean of 47.12 (millions) and a standard deviation of 7.72 (millions). What is the probability that the number of shares traded on a particular day, selected at random, will be a) between the mean and 60 million shares?

Answer

Table V provides us with probabilities associated with specific values of z. Therefore, we must first transform the raw scores into z - scores.

The z - score corresponding to X = 60 is:

$$= \frac{60 - 47.12}{7.72} = 1.67$$

Referring to Column B, Table V, we see that the proportion of area between the mean and a z - score of 1.67 is 0.4525. Thus, the probability of randomly selecting a day in which the number of shares traded was between 47.12 and 60 million is approximately 45 percent.

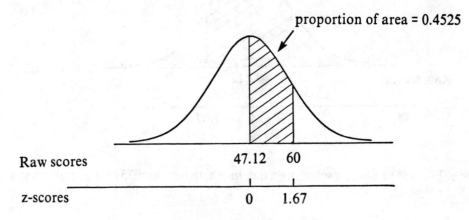

b) between the mean and 35 million shares?

Answer

The z- score corresponding to X = 35 is:

$$z = \frac{35 - 47.12}{7.72} = -1.57$$

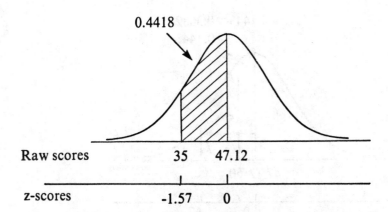

Negative z- scores have exactly the same proportions of area as their positive counterparts. Why? Because the normal curve is symmetrical about the mean. Thus, we find the area between the mean and z = -1.57 by looking in Column B for z = 1.57. We find this proportion to be 0.4418.

c)   between 35 and 60 million shares?

Answer

To find the proportion of area between two points when they are on *different* sides of the mean, we find the corresponding proportions of area between each point and the mean. We then simply add these proportions together.

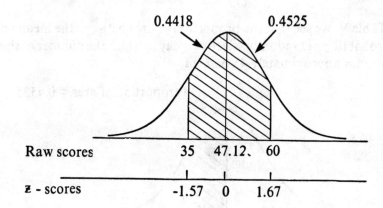

Thus, the probability of randomly selecting a day in which between 35 and 60 million shares were sold is 0.4418 + 0.4525 = 0.8943.

d)   between 50 and 60 million shares?

Answer

First, we find the z- scores and the corresponding proportions of area:

   X = 50, z = 0.37, proportion of area = 0.1443
   X = 60, z = 1.67, proportion of area = 0.4525

We can see from the figure below that the proportion of area between these two values can be found by subtraction.

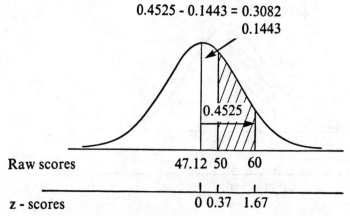

e)   between 20 and 30 million shares?

Answer

The procedures here are the same as in d). We find the proportion of area corresponding to each z and subtract to find the proportion of area between the two values.

38

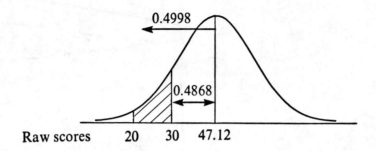

Raw scores   20   30   47.12

Thus, the probability of randomly selecting a day in which the number of shares traded was between 20 and 30 million is:

$$0.4998 - 0.4868 = 0.0130$$

f)   more than 50 million shares?

Answer

We may find this probability directly from Column C of Table V. We previously found that z = 0.37 for X = 50. Thus, the proportion area beyond a z of 0.37 is 0.3557.

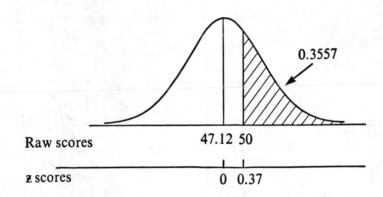

Raw scores   47.12 50

z scores   0 0.37

Answers

2.   P = 0.40, n = 20, p(x ⩾ 10) = 0.2447.

3.   Job #1   P = 0.30, n = 6, p (x ⩾ 2) = 0.5797
        Job #2   P = 0.50, n = 5, p (x ⩾ 3) = 0.4999

4.   (a) $\mu = (2496)\left(\dfrac{1}{480}\right) = 5.2$

    (b) p (x > 9) = 0.0220 + 0.0104 + 0.0045 + 0.0018 + 0.0007 + 0.0002 + 0.0001

             = 0.0397

5.   (a) To find λ (the expected average number born per hour), divide 12 by 24. We find that λ = 0.5. Thus, since t = 1, μ = 0.5. Looking up μ = 0.5 in Table IV and x = 2, we find p(x) = 0.0758.

    (b) p(x=2) = 0.0758; p(x=3) = 0.0126; p(x=4) = 0.0016; p(x=5) = 0.0002. Thus, p(x⩾2) = 0.0758 + 0.0126 + 0.0016 + 0.0002 = 0.0902. The probability is about 9 in 100 that 2 or more children will be born during any given hour.

"...Have the feminists gone too far? You'll have to ask my wife—
she'll be home from work soon."

"I have listened to the voice of the people...but I have decided
to run again, anyway!"

Chapter 6

Sampling and Sampling Distribution

Lesson 6-1 What Can Go Wrong with a Survey?

The survey is one of the quickest, least expensive ways to obtain information needed to improve the quality of business, political, and economic decisions. Its widespread use testifies to the fact that many consider the survey a vital instrument for gaining information. As with any other business instrument, it cannot be applied willy nilly to any situation where there is an information gap. More specifically, it shows to greatest advantage when the respondents are not threatened by the content. A greater number of people are willing to answer the questions and their answers are likely to be honest. In contrast, if the survey deals with sensitive topics in which the person feels threatened in any way, many respondents may refuse to participate. Those refusing may differ in significant ways from those who agree to participate. Thus, the most sophisticated sampling techniques may be compromised since the final sample may contain an unknown and/or unquantifiable source of bias.

Some of the types of questionnaires that may be threatening include:

> *personal dimensions*, e.g., sexual practices, attitudes about minority or majority groups, and in some people, political views.

> *threat to ego*, e.g., surveys that reveal educational achievement, intellectual or cultural sophistication. In many cases, the respondent may not refuse to answer, but may slant the answers so as to convey a favorable impression on the interviewer.

> *threat to economic status*, e.g., political leaders may refuse to answer questions concerning crime rate because of possible adverse effects on businesses planning to locate in the community. Indeed, many so-called crime statistics are little more than fiction because of community "stonewalling."

Even if the survey deals with a nonsensitive topic, its validity may be undermined by use of a faulty instrument. For example, if a questionnaire format is used, care must be taken to avoid the use of loaded words, leading questions, etc. A person who asks "Are you in favor of Senator Frump's far-reaching and insightful legislation on aging?" may already have influenced the answer.

Lesson 6-2 Why Use the Finite Population Correction Factor?

As we pointed out in the chapter, very few investigators use sampling with replacement. Consequently, when we are dealing with finite populations, the withdrawal of each element in the population reduces the variability of the population prior to the next draw. This is due to the fact that there is one less element in the population. However, the larger the population, the less will be the effect of each element withdrawn. Of course, if the sample size is very large, even the variability of a large finite population will decrease as more elements are withdrawn. This is why the ratio of the sample size to the population is used in establishing a rule of thumb about where to apply the *fcf*.

The *fcf* is not applied when sampling from infinite populations because the population remains infinite even when elements are withdrawn from it.

Multiple-Choice Items

1. If we obtained a sample of 500 registered voters and ascertained their selections in a coming election, our interest would focus on: a) how the membership of the sample would vote; b) estimating the voting preferences of the population from which the sample was drawn; c) estimating the voting preferences of a population larger than the one from which the sample was drawn; d) none of the above.

2. We usually elect to obtain samples rather than a census because of: a) economic factors; b) time considerations; c) logistical problems; d) all of the above.

3. If a member of Congress uses the incoming mail to judge the pulse of his or her constituency, the method of sampling is: a) convenience; b) quota; c) random selection; d) judgmental sampling.

4. Which of the following represent sampling error? a) presence of uncontrolled variables; b) a poor measuring instrument; c) selection of sample from nontarget population; d) all of the above.

5. By increasing sample size, we will usually decrease: a) bias; b) errors due to a poor measuring instrument; c) sampling error; d) all of the above.

6. If the target population of interest consists of all adults eighteen years of age and older within a given community, telephone surveys are unlikely to reflect the target population because: a) those without telephones are not included; b) it leaves out people with unlisted numbers; c) it excludes people not at home when the call is made; d) all of the above.

7. Judgmental sampling: a) is too subjective to be useful; b) does not provide a random model by which to estimate sampling error; c) is a form of random sampling; d) is used when conducting the U.S. census.

8. Which of the following provides a more accurate method of selecting a simple random sample? a) use of a table of random digits; b) the lottery method; c) quota sampling; d) obtaining voluntary replies.

9. When we select random samples from each of several different subgroups, we are using: a) simple random sampling; b) quota sampling; c) judgmental sampling; d) stratified sampling.

10. There is a sampling distribution for the: a) mean; b) median; c) standard deviation; d) all of the above.

11. If we were to randomly select a large number of samples from a known population and were to calculate the mean of each, we would not be surprised to discover: a) that the sample means are identical to the population mean; b) that many sample means differ from the population mean; c) a distribution of sample means around some value other than the population mean; d) none of the above.

12. If we were to select an extremely large number of random samples of a fixed size from a normally distributed population, we would find that: a) the resulting probability distribution is normally distributed; b) the mean of the sample means would equal the population mean; c) the standard deviation of the sample means would be less than the population standard deviation; d) all of the above.

13. The relationship between the standard deviation of a sampling distribution of means and the standard deviation of the population is as follows:

a) $\sigma_{\bar{x}} = \dfrac{s}{\sqrt{n}};$

b) $s_{\bar{x}} = \dfrac{\sigma}{\sqrt{n}};$

c) $\sigma_{\bar{x}} = \dfrac{\sigma}{\sqrt{n}};$

d) $\sigma_{\bar{x}} = \dfrac{s}{n};$

14. The standard error of the mean of samples drawn from a normally distributed population: a) has the properties of the standard deviation of any normally distributed variable; b) bears no relation to the standard deviation of the parent population; c) has unique properties that do not permit the use of standard statistical tables; d) has properties that cannot be predicted from the parent population.

15. Given $\mu = 3.5$, $\sigma = 0.50$, and $\bar{X} = 3.0$, the z for $n = 25$ is: a) -5.0; b) 5.0; c) -0.50; d) 0.50.

16. Given that we are sampling from a non-normally distributed population, which sample size is likely to yield a distribution of means that approaches the normal probability distribution? a) n = 50; ;b) n = 10; c) n = 24; d) n = 2.

17. Estimated $\sigma_{\bar{x}}$ equals:

   a) $\dfrac{\sigma}{\sqrt{n}}$

   b) $\dfrac{s}{\sqrt{n}}$

   c) $\dfrac{\sigma}{\sqrt{n-1}}$

   d) $\dfrac{s}{\sqrt{n-1}}$

18. Use of the finite correction factor (fcf) should be considered: a) when the population is finite and the sample size is small; b) when the population is infinite and the sample size is large; c) when the population is finite and the sample size is large; d) when the population is infinite and the sample size is small.

19. The rule of thumb for deciding whether the finite correction factor should be used is the ratio:

   a) $\dfrac{N}{n}$;

   b) $\dfrac{N}{n-1}$;

   c) $\dfrac{n-1}{N}$;

   d) $\dfrac{n}{N}$.

20. When a sample has been selected in such a way that each member of the population has an equal chance of being chosen, our method employs: a) judgmental sampling; b) stratified sampling; c) simple random sampling; c) cluster sampling.

Answers: 1. b; 2. d; 3. a; 4. a; 5. c; 6. d; 7. b; 8. a; 9. d; 10. d; 11. b; 12. d; 13. c; 14. a; 15. a; 16. a; 17. b; 18. c; 19. d; 20. c.

Exercises

1. A Committee of Concerned Citizens suggests that police protection should be distributed according to crime rate in an area. That is, areas with high crime rates should have more police protection than areas with low crime rates. Suppose you were a member of this citizens' committee. Can you suggest a way to collect the data on people's attitudes toward the redistribution of police protection?

Answer: Let us look at some of the different sampling techniques.

Simple Random Sampling

Using this technique, the sample is selected in such a way so that every member of the population has an equal chance of being included. Suppose every member of the population was assigned a number. We could then use the table of random digits (Table VI) to select a sample of a specified size. Each random digit drawn would correspond to a specific member of the population. For example, suppose that there were 1,000 people in the population and you wanted a sample of 50. Each member would be assigned numbers 1 through 1,000. You would then randomly select a row in Table VI and those people whose numbers corresponded to the numbers in the Table would be included in your sample.

Systematic Random Sampling

A simpler way to achieve random sampling is to choose your sample according to some systematic method. For example, suppose you selected the first person randomly. You could then complete your sample of 50 by including every 20th person after the initial selection.

Stratified Sampling

You might wish to divide the city into various areas according to existing crime rates. You would then randomly select samples from each of these areas (or strata).

Cluster Sampling

In this case, you would divide the city into areas or blocks. You would then randomly select a block or area and interview every person in that area.

Convenience Sampling

Every member of the committee might be asked to interview their friends or relatives. Or the committee members might decide to conduct interviews over the telephone. This type of sampling is generally not representative of the population.

Judgmental Sampling

Based on previous experience, the committee might decide who to include in the survey as well as who *not* to include. They may judge that a preselected sample of 20 will give more information than a larger, but random, sample.

2. Rosemary has 460 employees. She wants to know how they will vote on a particular issue in an upcoming union election. However, she does not want to interview every member of the population. Therefore, she decides to survey a sample from this population. What sampling technique is she using if:

    (a) she looks over the list of employees and selects 10 that she feels knows the "pulse" of the staff.
    (b) she questions the first 10 employees she sees Monday morning.
    (c) she throws slips of paper with every employees' name into a big fishbowl, mixes them up, and picks out 10 names. She then questions these 10 people.

3. The life expectancy of a particular type of photocopy machine is normally distributed with a mean of five years and a standard deviation of 18 months. The manufacturer wants to run a special promotion and increase the warranty to four years. With repeated sampling, what is the probability that the mean life expectancy in the sample will be less than four years, given the following sample sizes:

    (a) 9
    (b) 16
    (c) 20

4. Suppose we have a population with 112 members (i.e., N = 112) and μ = 107.2, and σ = 7.15.

    Let us now take a different size sample and determine the probability that the obtained sample mean will be as high as 110.

    (a) n = 10
    (b) n = 25
    (c) n = 100

    Comment on the effects of increased sample size.

Answers

2. (a) judgmental
    (b) convenience
    (c) simple random

3. (a) n = 9

$$s_{\bar{x}} = \frac{s}{\sqrt{n}} = \frac{18}{\sqrt{9}} = 6$$

$$z = \frac{48 - 60}{6} = -2.00$$

(Table V, Column C) p = 0.0228 or 2.28 probability.

(b) n = 16

$$s_{\bar{x}} = \frac{18}{\sqrt{16}} = 4.5$$

$$z = \frac{48-60}{4.5} = -2.67$$

p = 0.0038 or 0.38 percent probability.

(c) n = 20

$$s_{\bar{x}} = \frac{18}{\sqrt{20}} = 4.03$$

$$z = \frac{-12}{4.03} = -2.98$$

p = 0.0014 or 0.14 percent probability.

4. Since we are dealing with a small, finite population, we shall use the finite correction factor in calculating the standard errors of the mean.

(a)
$$\sigma_{\bar{x}} = \frac{7.15}{\sqrt{10}} \left(\sqrt{\frac{112-10}{111}} \right) = (2.26)(0.9586) = 2.17$$

$$z = \frac{110 - 107.2}{2.17} = 1.29; \quad p = 0.0985$$

(b)
$$\sigma_{\bar{x}} = \frac{7.15}{\sqrt{25}} \left(\sqrt{\frac{112-25}{111}} \right) = (1.43)(0.8853) = 1.27$$

$$z = \frac{110 - 107.2}{1.27} = 2.20; \quad p = 0.0139$$

(c)

$$\sigma_{\bar{x}} = \frac{7.15}{\sqrt{50}}\left(\sqrt{\frac{112-50}{111}}\right) = (1.01)(0.7476) = 0.78$$

$$z = \frac{110 - 107.2}{0.78} = 3.59; \quad p = 0.0002$$

We see two distinct effects of increased sample size. First, the larger the sample, the smaller the uncorrected standard error of the mean. Second, the larger the sample size in relation to the size of the population, the greater the impact of the finite correction factor.

Lesson 7-1 A Word about Sufficient Estimators

In the text, we discussed three characteristics of a good estimator: It is unbiased, efficient and consistent. A fourth characteristic is that the sample statistic be a sufficient estimator. To illustrate, imagine that we are attempting to estimate the parameter γ from the statistic v. We say that v is a sufficient estimator of the parameter γ, if the statistic contains all the information about the parameter that is in the data. We cannot improve our estimate by utilizing any aspect of the data that is not already included in the sample statistic, v. Stated another way, imagine we were to calculate another statistic, f, from the sample data. Now imagine a conditional distribution of f, given the value of v. If the conditional distribution of f, given v, is independent of the value of γ, then v is a sufficient estimator.

To illustrate. When samples are drawn from a Bernoulli distribution, p is a sufficient estimator of P since there is no additional information that would make p a better estimator of P.

It should be noted that it is not always possible to find a sufficient estimator. However, when one is found, it is usually possible to find an unbiased and efficient estimator.

Lesson 7-2   Confidence Interval Bands for the Population Proportion

Suppose that we obtain a random sample from a two category variable and obtain a sample proportion, p. This is an unbiased point estimate of the population, P. We wish also to establish an interval which, with repeated samples, would bracket the population proportion a specified proportion of the time. To construct confidence intervals for P directly from the binomial distribution would require a prodigious amount of computational work. For large samples, the normal approximation to the binomial is usually used for establishing the confidence interval of the population proportion, P.

However, for most purposes, graphic devices may be used to approximate the upper and lower bands for varying sample proportions(p), at varying n's, and for different confidence coefficients. These are usually available in mathematics libraries.

The following table illustrates the use of one of these graphs. It shows the 95 percent confidence interval bands for varying values of p and for selected values of n.

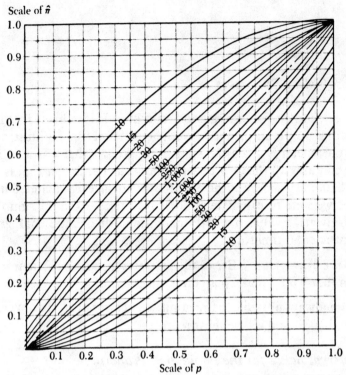

Source: This chart is reproduced with the permission of Professor E. S. Pearson from C. J. Clopper and E. S. Pearson, "The Use of Confidence or Fiducial Limits Illustrated in the Case of the Binomial," *Biometrika*, vol. 26 (1934), p. 404.

95 percent confidence interval bands for the population proportion, P.

To use the table, locate the obtained sample proportion on the horizontal axis labelled scale of p. Construct a vertical line until it intercepts the approximate sample size. Move to the left vertical axis to obtain the lower band at the 95 percent confidence interval. Then return to the horizontal axis and continue the vertical line until it intercepts the appropriate n for the upper band. Again read left to obtain the upper band. To illustrate, if n = 100, p = 0.70, we find the lower band to be approximately 0.61 and the upper band to be approximately 0.78. It should be noted that the interval estimates are exact. However, small errors are likely due to the fact that we are estimating the values from a chart.

Multiple-Choice Items

1. If the variability of the sampling distribution of one estimator is less than that of another, then it is said to be a more _____ estimator. a) consistent; b) efficient; c) unbiased; d) none of the above.

2. The numerical value used to estimate a parameter is a(n): a) estimate; b) estimator; c) sufficient estimator; d) consistent estimator.

3. A random sample of department store sales of a new item reveals that the mean number of sales is 25 per store per week. If these figures are used to project future sales: a) the mean is the estimate and 25 is the estimator; b) the mean is the estimator and 25 is the estimate; c) both the mean and 25 are estimates; d) both the mean and 25 are estimators.

4. When you estimate a person's height to be 6' give or take two inches, you have made: a) a point estimate; b) an interval estimate; c) both a point and an interval estimate; d) none of the above.

5. Which of the following is *not* true? An interval estimate: a) yields the probability that the parameter is a value between the upper and lower limits of an interval; b) expresses a degree of confidence that the banding values include the parameter; c) will include the parameter a specific proportion of the time following many random samplings; d) none of the above.

Which of the following does not illustrate a bias?

a)   b)   c)   d)

7. When using a sample statistic as an estimator, increasing n: a) decreases consistency; b) increases consistency in a linear fashion; c) decreases consistency in a linear fashion; d) increases consistency in a nonlinear fashion.

8. Given a population standard deviation, which of the following increases in sample size is likely to have the greatest effect on the standard error of the mean? a) from 10 to 20; b) from 40 to 50; c) from 500 to 550; d) from 1,000 to 1,200.

9. An individual states: I feel 90 percent confident that the parameter is between 80 and 100. a) 80 and 100 are confidence coefficients; b) 90 is the confidence coefficient in which the upper value is 100 and the lower 80; c) 80 is the lower confidence coefficient and 100 the upper coefficient; d) none of the above.

10. When σ is known and n is large, the general formula for the 95 percent confidence interval is: a) $\overline{X} \pm 1.96\ s_{\overline{x}}$; b) $\mu \pm 1.96\ s_{\overline{x}}$; c) $\overline{X} \pm 2.33\ s_{\overline{x}}$; d) $\overline{X} \pm 1.96\ \sigma_{\overline{x}}$.

11. To increase the precision of an interval estimate, we may: a) decrease the sample size; b) increase the sample size; c) change to a less demanding confidence coefficient; d) none of the above.

12. When σ is unknown and n is less than 30: a) the approximation of s to σ is good; b) the standard normal curve may be used in establishing interval estimates; c) the approximation of s to σ is poor; d) there is no acceptable means of approximating the value of σ.

13. If the sum of four numbers is 23, and the value of the numbers are 4, 5, and 9 respectively, the value of the fourth number is: a) 9; b) 5; c) 3; d) none of the above.

14. Referring to item 13, the number of degrees of freedom is: a) 4; b) 23; c) 22; d) 3.

15. The finite population correction factor should be used when: a) the sample size is large; b) the sample is 5 percent or more of the population size; c) the sample is large and the population is infinite; d) the sample is small and the population is infinite.

16. If pairs of samples of the same sample size are randomly drawn from the same population, the mean of the sampling distribution is:

a)   greater than 1.00
b)   0
c) $\dfrac{s_1{}^2 - s_2{}^2}{2}$
d)   insufficient information to answer.

17. If n = 100, x = 40 and n-x = 60: a) p = 0.36, $\overline{q}$ = 0.67; b) p = 0.60, q = 0.40; c) p = 0.50, q = 0.50; d) none of the above.

18. Referring to item 17, $s_{\bar{p}}$ equals:

a) $\sqrt{\dfrac{0.24}{100}}$

b) $\sqrt{\dfrac{0.24}{10}}$

c) $\sqrt{\dfrac{2.40}{100}}$

d) none of the above.

19. If we do not know the population standard deviation: a) we cannot estimate the desired sample size; b) we may estimate the desired sample size only if we have a sample standard deviation; c) we may estimate the desired sample size if we have either a sample standard deviation or we have an estimate of the range; d) none of the above.

20. If the range of the values of a variable is 80, a crude estimate of the population standard deviation is: a) 20; b) 16; c) 9; d) cannot be estimated.

Answers: 1. b; 2. a; 3. d; 4. c; 5. a; 6. b; 7. d; 8. a; 9. b; 10. d; 11. b; 12. c; 13. b; 14. d; 15. b. 16. b; 17. d; 18. a; 19. c; 20. a.

Exercises

1. A random sample of 9 textbooks on Business Management showed that the mean number of pages was 600 with a standard deviation of 25. What are the 95 percent confidence limits for the mean number of pages?

2. The California Highway Patrol decides to study the driving speed of cars on the freeway. A sample of 121 cars reveals a mean driving speed of 58 mph with s = 6. Find the 99 percent confidence limits for driving speed of all cars.

3. Mark F., is training a trotter named "Rodney the Rat" for a big race. A sample of 30 sessions reveals Rodney's average time is 2 minutes 4 seconds (2:04) with s = 1.5 seconds. Find the 95 percent confidence limits for Rodney's true time.

4. In a sample of 200 horses trained by Mark F., 160 have made it to the "winners circle." Find the 95 percent confidence limits for the proportion of horses who win.

5. Eugene F., the new chairman of the Board of G.S.I., finds that, in a sample of 90 employees at one of their facilities, 10 are female. a) Find the 99 percent confidence limits for the proportion of female employees. b) Suppose the chairman wants to be 95 percent sure that the sample proportion differs from the population proportion by no more than 0.05. What size sample should he take?

Answers

1. We use Formula (7.3) to determine the confidence interval when σ is unknown and the sample is small:

$$\bar{X} \pm t_{df}s_{\bar{x}}$$

Since n = 9, df = 8, t_{df} = 2.064

$$s_{\bar{x}} = \frac{s}{\sqrt{n}} = \frac{25}{\sqrt{9}} = 8.33$$

Thus, the 95 percent confidence interval is:

$$600 \pm (2.064)(8.33) = 600 \pm 17.19$$
$$= 582.81 \text{ to } 617.19$$

2.
$$s_{\bar{x}} = \frac{6}{\sqrt{121}} = 0.55$$

$$t_{df} = 2.617$$

$$58 \pm (2.617)(0.55) = 58 \pm 1.44$$
$$= 56.56 \text{ to } 59.44$$

3.
$$s_{\bar{x}} = \frac{1.5}{\sqrt{30}} = 0.2739$$

$$t_{df} = 2.045$$

$$124 \pm (2.045)(0.2739) = 124 \pm 0.56$$
$$= 123.44 \text{ to } 124.56 \text{ seconds}$$

4.
$$\bar{p} = \frac{160}{200} = 0.80, \bar{q} = 0.20$$

$$s_{\bar{p}} = \sqrt{\frac{(0.80)(0.20)}{200}} = 0.0283$$

$$\bar{p} \pm z\, s_{\bar{p}}$$

95 percent confidence limits = $0.80 \pm 1.96\,(0.0283)$
$$= 0.80 \pm 0.06$$
$$= 0.74 \text{ to } 0.86$$

5. a)
$$\bar{p} = \frac{10}{90} = 0.1111, \bar{q} = 0.8889$$

$$s_{\bar{p}} = \sqrt{\frac{(0.1111)(0.8889)}{180}} = 0.0234$$

99 percent confidence limits = $0.1111 \pm 2.58\,(0.0234)$
$$= 0.1111 \pm 0.0604$$
$$= 0.0507 \text{ to } 0.1715$$

b) $n = \left(\frac{1.96}{0.05}\right)^2 (0.1111)\,(0.8889) = 151.8$ or approximately 152

"What big financial deal? . . . They're figuring out how many calories they had for lunch!"

Chapter 8

Lesson 8-1 Basic Concepts

In this chapter, we looked at a broad and sometimes confusing array of procedures for testing statistical hypotheses. We looked at tests involving both means and proportions. Some tests involved a single sample, others involved two independent samples and still others were comparisons between correlated samples. Moreover, because of the Central Limit Theorem, the normal curve may be used as the sampling distribution when the sample size is large. The following table summarizes the standard error formulas, the test statistics, and the sampling distributions used in testing various statistical hypotheses.

Comparisons	Number of Groups	Sample Size	Standard Error	Test Statistic	Sampling Distribution
Means	single	large	$\dfrac{s}{\sqrt{n}}$	$z = \dfrac{\bar{X} - \mu_o}{s_{\bar{x}}}$	normal curve
		small	$\dfrac{s}{\sqrt{n}}$	$t = \dfrac{\bar{X} - \mu_o}{s_{\bar{x}}}$	student t distribution
	two independent groups	large	$\sqrt{\dfrac{n_1 s^2_1 + n_2 s^2_2}{n_1 n_2}}$	$z = \dfrac{\bar{X}_1 - \bar{X}_2}{s_{\bar{x}_1 \bar{x}_2}}$	normal curve
		small	$\sqrt{\dfrac{n_1 s^2_1 + n_2 s^2_2}{n_1 n_2}}$	$t = \dfrac{\bar{X}_1 - \bar{X}_2}{s_{\bar{x}_1 \bar{x}_2}}$	student t distribution
	correlated samples	small and large	$\sqrt{\dfrac{\Sigma d^2 - \dfrac{(\Sigma d)^2}{n}}{n(n-1)}}$	$t = \dfrac{\bar{d}}{s_{\bar{d}}}$	student t distribution
Proportions	single	large	$\sqrt{\dfrac{\bar{p}\bar{q}}{n}}$	$z = \dfrac{\bar{p} - P_o}{s_{\bar{p}}}$	normal curve
		small	use binomial		
	two independent groups		$\sqrt{pq\left(\dfrac{1}{n_1} + \dfrac{1}{n_2}\right)}$	$z = \dfrac{\bar{p}_1 - \bar{p}_2}{s_{\bar{p}_1 - \bar{p}_2}}$	normal curve

Multiple-Choice Items

1. Which of the following is an acceptable statement of a null hypothesis? a) sample proportion 1 is equal to sample proportion 2; b) the true difference between the sample means is zero; c) the samples were drawn from populations with the same mean; d) the true proportion of registered Republican voters in the sample is 0.51.

2. A group of 20 individuals are assigned at random to two independent groups. How many degrees of freedom are used in evaluating the significance of the difference? a) 18; b) 20; c) 19; d) 21.

3. Which of the following are acceptable paired null and alternative hypotheses? a)$H_o:\mu_1 = \mu_2$, $H_1:\mu_1 > \mu_2$; b) $H_o:\overline{X}_1 = \overline{X}_2$, $H_1: \overline{X}_1 \neq \overline{X}_2$; c) $H_o:\mu_1 \leqslant \mu_2$, $H_1:\mu_1 < \mu_2$; d) $H_o:\mu_1 = \mu_2$, $H_1:\mu_1 \neq \mu_2$.

4. If H_o is true and we reject H_o, we have: a) made a Type I error; b) drawn a correct conclusion; c) made a Type II error; d) cannot say without more information.

5. If H_o is false and we reject H_o, we have: a) made a Type I error; b) drawn a correct conclusion; c) made a Type II error; d) cannot say without more information.

6. If H_o is false and we reject H_o, we have: a) made a Type I error; b) drawn a correct conclusion; c) made a Type II error; d) cannot say without more information.

7. If H_o is true and we fail to reject H_o, we have: a) made a Type I error; b) drawn a correct conclusion; c) made a Type II error; d) cannot say without more information.

8. Which of the following is a directional alternative hypothesis? a) $P_1 \neq P_2$; b) $\mu_1 \neq \mu_2$; c) $\mu_1 < \mu_2$; d) all of the above.

9. Which of the following could serve as a null hypothesis in the one sample case? a) $\mu_1 = \mu_2$; b) $\mu = \mu_o$; c) $\overline{X}_1 = \mu_o$; d) $\overline{X}_1 = \overline{X}_2$.

10. Which of the following could serve as a null hypothesis in the two sample cases: a) $\mu = \mu_o$; b) $\overline{X}_1 = \overline{X}_2$; c) $\overline{X}_1 = \mu_2$; d) $\mu_1 = \mu_2$.

Items 11-13 refer to the following information:

$$\overline{X}_1 = 50 \qquad \overline{X}_2 = 35$$

$$s_1 = 10 \qquad s_2 = 10$$

$$n_1 = 50 \qquad n_2 = 50$$

11. $s_{\overline{X}_1 - \overline{X}_2}$ equals: a) 2; b) 4; c) 0.62; d) $\sqrt{2}$.

12. The most likely null hypothesis is: a) $\overline{X}_1 = \overline{X}_2$; b) $\mu_o = 42.5$; c) $\mu_1 > \mu_2$; d) $\mu_1 = \mu_2$.

13. The appropriate test of significance involves: a) large sample, two independent groups; b) large sample, one group; c) small sample, two independent groups; d) small sample, one group.

14. In a matched group design with 21 subjects in each group, degrees of freedom equal: a) 19; b) 42; c) 30; d) 20.

15. Given: $\Sigma d = 40$, $\Sigma d^2 = 270$, $n = 20$, $\overline{d}$ equals: a) 14; b) 2; c) 70; d) 1.56.

16. Referring to item 15, s_d equals: a) 10; b) 100; c) $\sqrt{10}$; d) $\sqrt{9.5}$.

17. To test the null hypothesis that the sample proportion was selected from a population with a given P, when $n < 30$: a) use two sample test for large samples; ; b) use the binomial distributions; c) use the single sample test for large samples; d) none of the above.

18. If $\bar{p} = 0.20 +$ $s_p = .04$, $P_o = 0.16$, and $n > 40$, z equals: a) 1.00; b) 40; c) 2.00; d) 9.50.

Answers   1. c; 2. a; 3. d; 4. a; 5. b; 6. b; 7. b; 8. c; 9. b; 10. d; 11. a; 12. d; 13. a; 14. d; 15. b; 16. c; 17. b; 18. a.

Exercises

1. The nutritionist at Silo High School contends that the students at her school consume more cola beverages than average. The mean number of grams consumed daily by teenagers is 280 grams. A random selection of 50 students reveals a mean daily consumption of 290 grams with s = 35. What does she conclude? Set this problem up in formal statistical terms and use $\alpha = 0.01$.

Answer

1. *Null hypothesis* (Ho): The population mean consumption of cola beverages for Silo High School students is equal to or less than the population for all teenagers, i.e., $\mu \leq \mu_o$.

2. *Alternative hypothesis* (H₁): Silo H. S. students consume more cola beverages than the population of all teenagers, i.e., $\mu > \mu_o$.

3. *Statistical Test:* We use the z-statistic since $n > 30$.

4. *Significance level:* $\alpha = 0.01$.

5. *Sampling distribution:* The normal probability distribution since, with $n > 30$, the sampling distribution of means approaches the form of the normal curve.

6. *Critical region:* Since H₁ is directional, the critical region consists of all values of $z \geq 2.33$.

   The z corresponding to $\bar{X} = 290$ is:

   $$z = \frac{\bar{X} - \mu_o}{s_{\bar{x}}} = \frac{290 - 280}{\frac{35}{\sqrt{50}}} = 2.02$$

Decision: Since the obtained z of 2.02 < 2.33, we fail to reject Ho. We cannot conclude that students at Silo H.S. are different with respect to cola consumption than teenagers in general.

2. The senior partner of a large public accounting firm believes that the wages of his staff members are different from the average. The mean weekly salary of all staff members nationally is $300. A random sample of 60 of his staff members showed a mean weekly salary of $325 with s = $45.

   What do you conclude? Use $\alpha = 0.05$. Set this problem up in formal statistical terms.

3. A real estate broker tells Mr. and Mrs. Manfried that the children living in Phase III of a condominium project are younger than the average. The mean age of all children living in the entire project is 11.5. Listed below are the ages of 10 children living in Phase III.

   What do you conclude? Use $\alpha = 0.05$. (Set this problem up in formal statistical terms).

8	6
16	3
7	17
10	14
4	9

4. A shirt manufacturer wants to determine whether a new type of machine has changed the production output of his employees. Previously, the mean production was 28 pieces per hour. Using the new machine, the mean output of 20 randomly selected employees is 29.5 with s = 2.5. Employing $\alpha = 0.1$, what does he conclude? (Set this problem up in formal statistical terms.)

5. A comparison shopper wished to determine whether there was any difference in the amount of corn contained in 12 ounce cans produced by two different companies. She randomly selected 40 cans from each company and weighed the contents. She obtained the following results:

Company A	Company B
$\bar{X}_1 = 11.9$	$\bar{X}_2 = 12.2$
$s_1 = 3.2$	$s_2 = 3.9$

What did she conclude? Use $\alpha = 0.05$ and set this problem up in formal statistical terms.

6. In order to determine whether there is a significant difference between the hourly wages at two companies, the following data were obtained:

Company A	Company B
$\bar{X}_1 = \$8.25$	$\bar{X}_2 = \$8.75$
$s_1 = 1.25$	$s_2 = 1.40$
$n_1 = 12$	$n_2 = 15$

Use $\alpha = 0.01$, and set this problem up in formal statistical terms. What do you conclude?

7. Using a new technique, a sample of 100 items is randomly selected and tested for defectives. Five are found defective. In a randomly selected sample of 100 items using the old technique, seven are found defective. Use $\alpha = 0.05$ and determine whether there is a significant difference between the two techniques. Set this problem up in formal statistical terms.

8. The sales manager of a large dress manufacturing firm wishes to compare two different sales techniques. He randomly selects 50 customers who have been contacted via Technique 1 and find that 16 sales have been consummated. A random selection of 50 customers who have been exposed to Technique 2 reveals 22 sales. Is there a significant difference between the two techniques? Use $\alpha = 0.01$ and set this problem up in formal statistical terms.

Answers

2. *Null hypothesis* (H_o): The mean of the population from which the sample was drawn equals 300, i.e., $\mu = \mu_o$.

Alternative hypothesis (H_1): $\mu \neq \mu_o$.

Statistical test: z - statistic since n > 30

Significance level: $\alpha = 0.05$

Sampling distribution: The normal probability distribution.

Critical region: All values of $z \geqslant |1.96|$.

The z corresponding to $\overline{X} = 325$ is:

$$z = \frac{325 - 300}{\dfrac{45}{\sqrt{60}}} = 4.30$$

Decision: Since the obtained z exceeds the critical value, we reject H_o and affirm the senior partner's belief.

3. *Null hypothesis:* (H_o): $\mu \geqslant \mu_o$

   Alternative hypothesis: (H_1): $\mu < \mu_o$

   Statistical test: Student t-ratio since $n < 30$.

   Significance level: $\alpha = 0.05$

   Sampling distribution: t- distribution with df = 9

   Critical region: All values of $t \leqslant -1.833$

   $$\Sigma X = 94 \qquad\qquad \Sigma X^2 = 1096$$
   $$\overline{X} = 9.4 \qquad\qquad s = 4.86$$
   $$s_{\overline{X}} = \frac{4.86}{\sqrt{10}} = 1.54 \qquad t = \frac{9.4 - 11.5}{1.54} = -1.364$$

   Decision: Since the obtained t = -1.364 does not fall within the critical region, we fail to reject H_o.

4. *Null hypothesis* (H_1): $\mu = \mu_o$

   Alternative hypothesis (H_o): $\mu \neq \mu_o$

   Statistical test: Student t - ratio since $n < 30$.

   Significance level: $\alpha = 0.01$

   Sampling distribution: t - distribution with df = 19

   Critical region: All values of $t \geqslant | 2.861 |$

   $$s_{\overline{X}} = \frac{2.5}{\sqrt{20}} = 0.56$$

   $$t = \frac{29.5 - 28}{0.56} = 2.679$$

   Decision: Since the obtained t = 2.679 does not fall within the critical rgion, we fail to reject H_o.

5. *Null hypothesis* (H_o): There is no difference in the population mean weights of corn at the two companies, i.e., $\mu_1 = \mu_2$ or $\mu_1 - \mu_2 = 0$.

   Alternative hypothesis (H_1): There is a difference in the population mean weight of corn at the two companies, i.e., $\mu_1 \neq \mu_2$ or $\mu_1 - \mu_2 \neq 0$.

   Statistical test: Since we are comparing two large samples randomly selected from two different companies, the z - statistic for two independent samples is appropriate.

   Significance level: $\alpha = 0.05$

   Sampling distribution: The standard normal probability distribution.

Critical region: Since H_1 is nondirectional, the critical region consists of all values of $z \geqslant 1.96$ or $z \leqslant -1.96$.

$$s_{\bar{x}_1 - \bar{x}_2} = \sqrt{\frac{(3.2)^2}{40} + \frac{(3.9)^2}{40}} = 0.7977$$

$$z = \frac{11.9 - 12.2}{0.7977} = -0.38$$

Decision: Since the obtained z does not fall within the critical region, there is no statistically valid basis for asserting a difference in the mean weights of corn produced by the two companies.

6. *Null hypothesis* (H_o): $\mu_1 = \mu_2$

Alternative hypothesis (H_1): $\mu_1 \neq \mu_2$

Statistical test: t - ratio since we are dealing with small samples.

Significance level: $\alpha = 0.05$.

Sampling distribution: t - distribution with df = $n_1 + n_2 - 2$, or $12 + 15 - 2 = 25$.

Critical region: All values of $t \geqslant |2.060|$ or $t \geqslant 2.060$ or $t \leqslant -2.060$.

$$s_{\bar{x}_1 - \bar{x}_2} = \sqrt{\frac{12(1.25)^2 + 15(1.40)^2}{(12)(15)}} = 0.5172$$

$$t = \frac{8.25 - 8.75}{0.5172} = -0.967$$

Decision: Accept H_o.

7. *Null hypothesis* (H_o): Both sample proportions were drawn from the same population, i.e., $P_1 = P_2$ or $P_1 - P_2 = 0$.

Alternative hypothesis (H_1): Both sample proportions were selected from different populations, i.e., $P_1 \neq P_2$.

Statistical test: Since both n_1 and n_2 exceed 30, the z -statistic may be used.

Significance level: $\alpha = 0.05$.

Sampling distribution: The standard normal probability distribution.

Critical region: All values of $z \geqslant |1.96|$ or $z \geqslant 1.96$ or $z \leqslant -1.96$.

$$\bar{p}_1 = 0.05, \bar{p}_2 = 0.07$$

$$p = \frac{100(0.05) + 100(0.07)}{100 + 100} = 0.06$$

$$s_{\bar{p}_1 - \bar{p}_2} = \sqrt{(0.06)(0.94)\left(\frac{1}{100} + \frac{1}{100}\right)} = 0.0336$$

$$z = \frac{0.05 - 0.07}{0.0336} = -0.60$$

Decision: Accept H_o.

58

8.
$$\overline{p}_1 = \frac{16}{50} = 0.32 \qquad \overline{p}_2 = \frac{22}{50} = 0.44$$

$$p = \frac{50\,(0.32) + 50\,(0.44)}{50 + 50} = 0.38$$

$$s_{\overline{p}_1 - \overline{p}_1} = \sqrt{(0.38)(0.62)\left(\frac{1}{50} + \frac{1}{50}\right)} = 0.0971$$

$$z = \frac{0.32 - 0.44}{0.0971} = -1.24$$

Decision: Accept H_o.

"Ed, you're the only person I know who *always* makes money in the Stock Market. What's your secret?"

"I can tell you this much — get out of transportations and into industrials."

Lesson 9-1 Converting from Payoff Tables to Decision Trees

As we pointed out in the text, there are decision-making situations that are not easily developed in tabular form. This is particularly the case when different events affect the outcome of each decision or where decisions are made in a serial form, e.g., when the outcome of one decision affects the outcome of the next decision. The reverse is not true. Any decision analysis that is presented in tabular form can be readily converted to the form of a decision tree. To illustrate this point, we show below the decision tree counterpart.

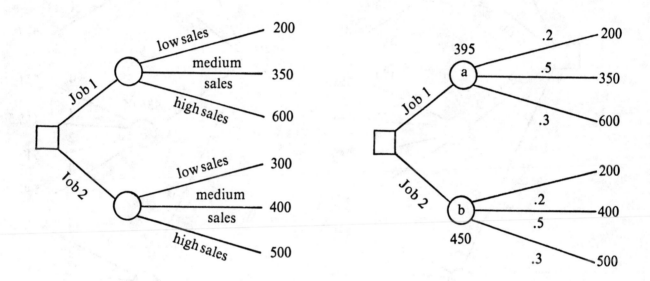

Decision tree analysis and backward induction for the data presented in Table 9.2 of the text.

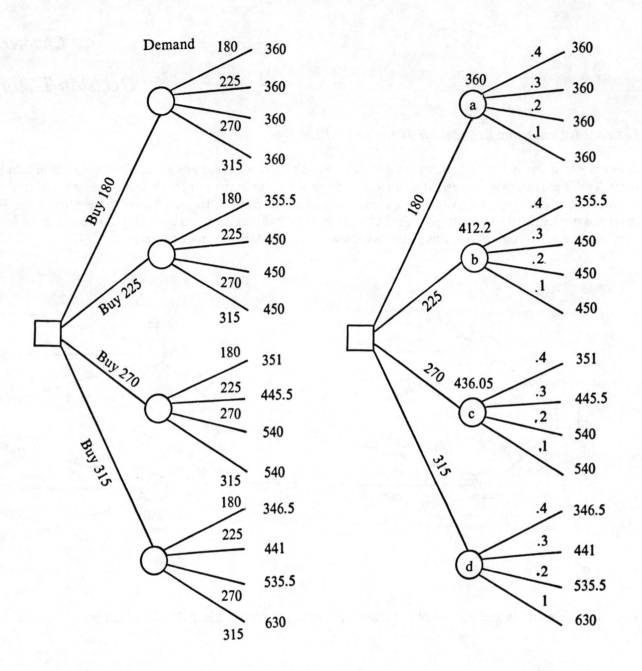

Decision tree analysis and backward induction from payoff tables 9. 10, 9.11, 9.12, and 9.13 of text:

Note that the decision tree can become quite cumbersome, when compared to the tabular presentation. This is the main reason that most decision analyists use both forms of analysis and presentation.

Multiple-Choice Items

1. Which of the following is most likely to be a state of nature? a) execute a buy order on the stock exchange; b) sell short in the commodities market; c) legislation enacted by the 98th Congree; d) support legislation proposed by the 98th Congress.

2. In order to conduct a decision analysis, we must have: a) a choice of alternatives; b) a way to measure payoff of choices; c) varying states of values; d) all of the above.

3. When an entrepreneur decides on a course of action based on its probability of success, the criterion used is a) utility; b) economic consequences; c) probability; d) probability and economic success together.

4. When a choice is made on the basis of factors other than long-range expected value, what criterion is used? a) utility; b) economic consequences; c) probability; d) probability and economic success together.

5. Another term for opportunity loss is: a) maximum gain; b) maximum loss; c) regret; d) minimum gain.

6. Which of the following probabilities might be used in a decision analysis? a) empirical; b) classical; c) subjective; d) all can be used.

7. When dealing with cost, the expected value of perfect information consists of: a) expected cost under perfect information minus the expected cost under uncertainty; b) expected gain under uncertainty minus the expected cost under uncertainty; c) expected cost under uncertainty minus the expected gain under uncertainty; d) expected cost under uncertainty minus the expected cost with perfect information.

8. The expected value of perfect information (EVPI) is the same as: a) the expected opportunity loss; b) the minimum gain possible; c) the maximum profit under minimum demand; d) the minimum profit under maximum demand.

9. The entrepreneur who states, "Assume the economy will be extremely poor over the next six months and tell me the maximum demand I can expect," is using the _____ criterion: a) minimum; b) maximin; c) minimax; d) maximax.

10. The minimax loss approach involves choosing: a) the maximum of a set of minimum opportunity losses; b) the maximum of a set of maximum opportunity losses; c) the minimum of a set of maximum opportunity losses; d) the minimum of a set of minimum opportunity losses.

Use the following table to answer items 11 through 15.

Demand	Order	Conditional Profit	Probability of Demand	Expected Profit
100	100	152	.50	
200	200	160	.30	
300	300	190	.15	
400	400	210	.05	

11. The expected profit based on a demand of 100 and an order of 100 is: a) 50; b) 304; c) 76; d) 200.

12. The expected profit based on a demand of 200 and an order of 200 is: a) 80; b) 48; c) 53.33; d) 90.

13. The expected profit based on a demand of 300 and an order of 300 is: a) 32.5; b) 28.5; c) 285; d) 200.

14. The expected profit based on a demand of 400 and an order of 400 is: a) 10.5; b) 800; c) 20; d) 42.

15. The optimum action: a) will be the most profitable; b) is the best decision, over the long run, in the face of uncertainty; c) sacrifices an opportunity to make a big profit in order to minimize risks; d) none of the above.

16. When action A dominates action B, we say: a) A is inadmissible as an alternative but cannot be eliminated; b) A is inadmissible as an alternative and can be eliminated; c) B is inadmissible as an alternative but cannot be eliminated; d) B is inadmissible as an alternative and may be eliminated.

17. Which of the following assumes the best state of nature? a) maximin; b) minimax; c) maximax; d) none of the above.

Given the following table, answer items 18-20.

Event	Prior Probability	Conditional Probability	Joint Probability	Revised Probability
B_1	.30		0.18	0.5625
B_2		0.20	0.12	0.3750
B_3	.20	0.10		___

18. The conditional probability of event B_1 is: a) 0.54; b) 1.67; c) 0.60; d) 0.17.

19. The prior probability of event B_2 is: a) 0.24; b) 1.67; c) 0.02; d) 0.60.

20. The revised probability of event B_3 is: a) 0.0625; b) 0.6250; c) 0.04; d) 0.10.

Answers: 1. c; 2. d; 3. c; 4. a; 5. c; 6. d; 7. d; 8. a; 9. b; 10. c; 11. c; 12. b; 13. b; 14. a; 15. b; 16. d; 17. c; 18. c; 19. d; 20. a.

Exercises

1. As the heating season approaches, a heating contractor must decide how many replacement units to order for customers who may need replacements during the winter. Any unit sold provides a $50 gross margin of profit. A unit that is unsold must be returned to the manufacturer at a fixed loss of $20 per unit. Based on previous experience, there are three possible demands that may occur: 100, 200, or 250 units.

   (a) Summarize this informtion into an initial payoff table.

Answer

Initial Payoff Table
Decisions or Actions

Demand	100	200	250
100	$5,000	$ 3,000	$ 2,000
200	5,000	10,000	9,000
250	5,000	10,000	12,500

   (b) Using the *maximin* criterion, what decision would the contractor make?

Answer

   (b) Using this criterion, we assume that the *worst* state of nature will occur; i.e., demand for 100 units. Thus, he would choose that action that leads to the maximum profit under this minimum demand. In this case, he would order 100 units.

   (c) Using the *maximax* criterion, what decision would he make?

Answer

Here we assume the *best* possible state of nature, i.e., demand for 250 units. Thus, the action leading to the maximum profit under this maximum demand: order 250 units.

   (b) Set up an opportunity loss table.

Answer

Opportunity Loss Table
Decisions or Actions
Order

Demand	100	200	250
100	0	2,000	3,000
200	5,000	0	1,000
250	7,500	2,500	0

(e) Using the *minimax* criterion, what decision would he make?

Answer

We choose the action in which the worst possible outcome (highest OL) is the least. Using this criterion, he would order 200 units since this decision has a maximum OL of $2,500 as compared with, say, 100 units which has a maximum opportunity loss of $7,500.

2. Suppose that, based on previous experience, the contractor assigns the following probabilities to the three possible events (or demand):

Demand	Probability
100	0.25
200	0.50
250	0.25

(a) Which action provides the maximum expected payoff?

Answer

We can calculate the expected value of each decision by multiplying each payoff by its associated probability and obtaining the sum over all values of that decision. This sum represents the expected value of that decision.

Decisions or Actions

	Order 100			Order 200			Order 250		
	Payoff	*Probability*	*Payoff x Probability*	*Payoff*	*p*	*Payoff x p*	*Payoff*	*p*	*Payoff x p*
100	5,000	0.25	1,250	3,000	0.25	750	2,000	0.25	500
200	5,000	0.50	2,500	10,000	0.50	5,000	9,000	0.50	4,500
250	5,000	0.25	1,250	10,000	0.25	2,500	12,500	0.25	3,125
	Expected payoff		$5,000			$8,250			$8,125

Thus, in terms of maximizing expected monetary gain, he should order 200 units since, over the long run, he will make more money.

(b) Which action provides the minimum expected opportunity loss?

Answer

Using the same procedures as in a), we can determine the expected opportunity loss for each decision.

Decisions or Actions

		Order 100		Order 200		Order 250	
Demand	*p*	*OL*	*OLxp*	*OL*	*OLxp*	*OL*	*OLxp*
100	0.25	0	0	2,000	500	3,000	750
200	0.50	5,000	2,500	0	0	1,000	500
250	0.25	7,500	1,875	2,500	625	0	0
	Expected OL		$4,375		1,125		1,250

The decision made on the basis of minimizing opportunity loss is the same decision made on the basis of maximizing expected monetary gain, i.e., order 200 units.

(c) Calculate the expected value of perfect information (EVPI).

Answer

In order to figure the EVPI, we assume we make the "correct" decision each time.

	Decisions								
	Order 100			Order 200			Order 250		
100	5,000	0.25	1,250	—	—	—	—	—	—
200	—	—	—	10,000	0.50	5,000	—	—	—
250	—	—	—	—	—	—	12,500	0.25	3,125

The expected profit with perfect information = 1,250 + 5,000 + 3,125 = 9,375. A decision made under uncertainty (see #2a) yielded an expected profit of $8,250. Thus, EVPI = 9,375 - 8,250 = $1,125. Therefore, it's worth up to $1,125 to eliminate uncertainty.

3. Suppose that the heating contractor decides to hire an independent research organization to sample his customers and obtain an estimate of the number of units they are likely to order. The prior record of success of this organization is shown below:

	Prediction order		
Demand (D_1)	100	200	250
Actually 100	0.85	0.10	0.05
Actually 200	0.10	0.80	0.10
Actually 250	0.10	0.20	0.70

(a) Calculate the revised probabilities based on the research firm's predictions.

Answer

Let us calculate the revised probabilities for each of the firm's predictions.

I. Calculation of revised probabilities based on firm's prediction of 100 units ordered (P_1):

Demand	Prior p	Conditional p $p(P_i \mid D_i)$	Joint p $p(D_1)p(P_1 \mid D_i)$	Revised p $p(D_i \mid P_1)$
100	0.25	0.85	0.2125	0.7391
200	0.50	0.10	0.0500	0.1739
250	0.25	0.10	0.0250	0.0870
			0.2875	1.0000

The probability that the firm will predict demand of 100 units, i.e., p (P_1) = 0.2875.

II. Calculation of revised probabilities based on firm's prediction of 200 units ordered (P_2):

Demand	Prior p	Condition p $p(P_2 \mid D_i)$	Joint p $(D_1)p(P_2 \mid D_i)$	Revised p $p(D_i \mid P_2)$
100	0.25	0.10	0.0250	0.0526
200	0.50	0.80	0.4000	0.8421
250	0.25	0.20	0.0500	0.1053
			0.4750	1.0000

The probability that the firm will predict a demand of 200 units, i.e., p (P_2) = 0.4750.

III. Calculation of revised probabilities based on firm's prediction of 250 units ordered (P_3):

Demand	Prior p	Conditional p $p(P_3|D_i)$	Joint p $p(D_i)p(P_3|D_i)$	Revised p $p(D_i|P_3)$
100	0.25	0.05	0.0125	0.0526
200	0.10	0.10	0.0500	0.2105
250	0.70	0.70	0.1750	0.7368
			0.2375	0.9999

The probability that the firm will predict a demand of 250 units, i.e., $p(P_3) = 0.2375$.

(b) What decision should the contractor make if the firm predicts 100, 200, or 250 units?

Answer

If the firm predicts 100 units (P_1), the expected profit for an order of 100 units is:

$$(0.7391)(5,000) + (0.1739)(5,000) + (0.0870)(5,000) = \$5,000.00$$

The expected profit for 200 units is:

$$(0.7391)(3,000) + (0.1739)(10,000) + (0.0870)(10,000) = \$4,826.30$$

and the expected profit for a 250 unit order is:

$$(0.7391)(2,000) + (0.1739)(9,000) + (0.0870)(12,500) = \$3,478.30$$

If the firm predicts 200 units (P_2), the expected profit for an order of 100 units is \$5,000 (confirm this);

The expected profit for a 200 unit order is:

$$(0.0526)(3,000) + (0.8421)(10,000) + (0.1053)(10,000) = \$9,631.80$$

and the expected profit for a 250 unit order is:

$$(0.0526)(2,000) + (0.8421)(9,000) + (0.1053)(12,500) = \$9,000.35$$

If the firm predicts 250 units (P_3), the expected profit for a 100 unit order is 5,000;

The expected profit for a 200 unit order is:

$$(0.0526)(3,000) + (0.2105)(10,000)+(0.7368)(10,000)=\$9,630.80$$

and the expected profit for a 250 unit order is:

$$(0.0526)(2,000)+(0.2105)(9,000)+(0.7368)(12,500)=\$11,209.70$$

The table below summarizes these results:

		Order 100	Order 200	Order 250
Firm's	P_1	5,000	4,826.30	3,478.30
prediction	P_2	5,000	9,631.80	9,630.80
	P_3	5,000	9,000.35	11,209.70

If the firm predicts 100 units, he should order 100 units.

If the firm predicts 200 units, he should order 200 units.

If the firm predicts 250 units, he should order 250 units.

(c) How much should the contractor pay for the firm's service?

Answer

In order to calculate the worth of the service, we compare the previously obtained payoff under uncertainty ($8,250) to the expected payoff using the service. We obtain this value by multiplying the profit associated with the decision dictated by the prediction by the probability of the prediction:

$p(P_1)$ (5,000) + $p(P_2)$ (9,631.80) + $p(P_3)$ (11,209.70) = (0.2875) (5,000) + (0.4750) (9,631.80) + (0.2375) (11,209.70) = 8,674.91

The difference between these two values [profit under uncertainty vs cost of using the service is the expected value of sample information (EVSI)].

$$EVSI = 8,674.91 - 8,250.00 = 424.91$$

Thus, the *most* the contractor should pay for this service is 424.91.

Lesson 10-1 A Word About Design

Earlier in the text we defined an experiment as "The process by which we obtain measurements or observations of different outcomes." This is a statistician's definition. In research settings, an experiment is defined in a far more restrictive fashion. What is often referred to as a "true experiment" has two essential characteristics:

(a) An experimental variable (condition or treatment) is administered to subjects, objects, or events. To illustrate, various amounts of a chemical substance may be added to different samples of molten ore to determine if the hardness of the metal is affected.

(b) The assignment of the subjects, objects, or events to the experimental conditions is random. In the above example, the batches of molten ore would be randomly assigned to the various experimental conditions. Thus, a specific amount of a given chemical substance would be added to all the batches assigned to one condition and different amounts would be added to the groups comprising the various experimental conditions.

The use of a "true experiment" permits strong conclusions to be drawn. Thus, if we were to find that one experimental condition produced significantly greater hardness levels of the metal, we would conclude that the amount of chemical substance added *caused* the increase in hardness. We can do this because the experimental subjects, objects, or events were treated alike in all ways except the administration of the experimental treatments. Moreover, since they were assigned at random to the experimental groups, we may presume that the experimental groups differed *only* in the treatments applied to them.

There are many so-called experiments that closely mimic the true experiment. What they lack, however, is random assignment to conditions and/or manipulation of the experimental treatment. Without these necessary features, strong conclusions cannot be drawn. To illustrate, a group of 92 coronary patients were studied for one year following their release from the hospital (Friedman, 1979). They were subsequently divided into two groups: dog owners and nonowners of dogs. It was found that 50 of 53 dog owners survived at least one year where only 28 of 39 of the nonowners achieved a one-year survival rate. The difference in survival rates was statistically significant. It is tempting to conclude that owning a dog somehow caused their masters to survive longer. However, the study was not a true experiment. The patients were not randomly assigned to the experimental conditions. In effect, they selected themselves. Nor was ownership of dogs manipulated by an experimenter. It is quite possible, even probable, that dog owners differ from nonowners of dogs in many ways other than dog ownership. They may exercise more (walking the dog), enjoy different life styles, experience less loneliness, to name but a few possibilities.

Many so-called experiments in business and economics are of this latter type. The experimental treatments may be variables that are naturally occurring and existed prior to the study. Comparisons of these pre-formed groups may or may not yield statistically significant differences. Even if the results are statistically significant, caution is advised against ascribing the differences to the experimental conditions.

Multiple-Choice Items

1. In a one-way analysis of variance, there is (are) _____ independent estimates of variability:
    a) one; b) two; c) three; d) the answer depends on the number of conditions.

2. Another way of representing $\Sigma(X-\overline{X})^2$ is:
   a) SS
   b) $\dfrac{SS}{n-1}$
   c) $X^2 - \overline{X}^2$
   d) none of the above

3. The within group variance estimate is: a) the variability between the various groups; b) the sum of squares within groups; c) the sum of squares between groups; d) the mean of the variances of each group.

4. If the between group variance estimate is large relative to the within group variance estimate: a) the F-ratio is large; b) the F-ratio is small, c) the F-ratio is unaffected; d) there is a large amount of random error.

5. When H_o is true, then F equals:

   a) $\dfrac{\sigma_a^2}{\sigma_\epsilon^2}$

   b) $\dfrac{\sigma\epsilon^2 + \sigma_a^2}{\sigma_a^2}$

   c) $\dfrac{\sigma_\epsilon^2}{\sigma_\epsilon^2}$

   d) $\dfrac{\sigma\epsilon^2 + \sigma_a^2}{\sigma_a^2}$

6. If df_{tot} = 60 and df_{bet} = 5, then df_w equals: a) 5; b) 55; c) 54; d) 57.

7. If n = 110, k = 7, df_w equals: a) 103; b) 104; c) 6; d) 3.

8. If n = 40, df_w = 34, the number of groups, k, equals: a) 4; b) 5; c) 6; d) 7.

9. As df increases, the critical value of F that marks off a given α-level: a) increases; b) stays the same; c) decreases; d) depends on the number of groups.

10. As df increases, the distribution of F: a) approaches normality; b) becomes positively skewed; c) becomes negatively skewed; d) remains the same.

11. If n = 20, k = 4, SS_w = 48; SS_{bet} = 30, then F equals: a) 1.6; b) 0.30; c) 2.5; d) 3.33.

12. If you obtained an F-ratio equal to 0.98 with df = 3,25, you should conclude that: a) there was a significant difference among the variances; b) you have made a computational error because F must equal at least 1.00; c) the variances within each group were homogeneous; d) the null hypothesis could not be rejected.

13. If the means for each treatment group were the same, the F-ratio would be: a) infinitely large; b) zero; c) a positive number between 0 and 100; d) depends on the magnitude of the means.

14. To obtain the between-group variance estimate, you divide SS_{bet} by: a) k-1; b) n; c) n-1; d) df_{tot}.

15. When using a one-way ANOVA with several groups, a disadvantage to conducting individual comparisons between pairs of experimental conditions is that: a) too many calculations are involved; b) there is an increased risk of a Type I error; c) there is an increased risk of a Type II error; d) all of the above.

16. When minor violations of the assumptions underlying a statistical test do not significantly alter the conclusion, the test is said to be: a) faulty; b) weak; c) compromised; d) robust.

17. A two-way analysis of variance permits: a) an analysis of the effects of variable 1; b) an analysis of the effects of variable 2; c) an analysis of joint effects of both variables; d) all of the above.

18. In a two-way analysis of variance, the between group variability may be partitioned into _____ components: a) one; b) two; c) three; d) depends on the number of within each variable.

19. If there are 5 levels of one variable and 4 levels of a second, the number of treatment combinations is: a) 9; b) 20; c) 12; d) 15.

20. In a randomized block design, we are primarily interested in: a) the effects of the blocks; b) the variability between blocks; c) the differences among levels of one treatment variable; d) the error term.

Answers: 1. b; 2. a; 3. d; 4. a; 5. c; 6. b; 7. a; 8. c; 9. c; 10. a; 11. d; 12. d; 13. b; 14. a; 15. b; 16. d; 17. d; 18. c; 19. b; 20. c.

Exercises

1. The sales manager of a large direct selling organization wishes to see whether any differences exist among four different selling strategies. She randomly assigns 20 salespeople to the four groups and records the number of successful contacts made by each person. She obtains the results shown:

Condition

X_1	X_2	X_3	X_4
3	10	2	3
4	6	4	4
6	8	1	5
7	5	2	4
3	3	1	5

(a) Set up and test H_o, using $\alpha = 0.05$.

(b) If warranted, test for significance of difference among paired means using $\alpha = 0.01$.

2. Let us assume that an investigator randomly assigns 16 subjects to four treatment combinations, i.e., four subjects per cell. The data are shown below:

	A_1		A_2		
	B_1	B_2	B_1	B_2	
	4	2	2	6	
	6	3	3	7	
	7	4	4	8	
	8	5	4	9	
sums	25	14	13	30	Total sum = 82

(a) Draw a graph of the means and judge whether an interaction is likely.

(b) Set up and test H_o, using $\alpha = 0.01$.

71

3. Imagine a three treatment design in which the treatments are randomly assigned within six blocks. The following presents the data:

Treatment Groups

Blocks	T_1	T_2	T_3	Sums
1	4	5	6	15
2	3	4	5	12
3	1	3	5	9
4	1	2	3	6
5	4	2	3	9
6	2	2	2	6
sums	15	18	24	57

Using $\alpha = 0.05$, perform a randomized block design analysis of variance.

Answers

1. H_o: $\mu_1 = \mu_2 = \mu_3 = \mu_4$

    H_1: At least one population mean is different from the others. Since we are using more than two independent groups, analysis of variance using the F-ratio is appropriate.

    Significance level: $\alpha = 0.05$.

    Sampling distribution: F with $df_{tot} = 19$, $df_{bet} = 3$, $df_w = 16$.

    Critical value: At $\alpha = 0.05$ and df = 3 and 19, the critical value for rejecting H_o is 3.24.

	X_1	X_1^2	X_2	X_2^2	X_3	X_3^2	X_4	X_4^2
	3	9	10	100	2	4	3	9
	4	16	6	36	4	16	4	16
	6	36	8	64	1	1	5	25
	7	49	5	25	2	4	4	16
	3	9	3	9	1	1	5	25
sums	23	119	32	234	10	26	21	91

$\Sigma X_{tot} = 23 + 32 + 10 + 21 = 86 \quad (\Sigma X_{tot})^2 = 7396$

$\dfrac{(\Sigma X_{tot})^2}{n} = \dfrac{7,396}{20} = 369.80$

$\Sigma X^2_{tot} = 119 + 234 + 26 + 91 + 470$

$$SS_{tot} = \Sigma X^2_{tot} - \frac{(\Sigma X_{tot})^2}{n}$$

$$= 470 - 369.80$$

$$= 100.20$$

$$SS_{bet} = \Sigma \frac{(\Sigma X_i)^2}{n_i} - \frac{(\Sigma X_{tot})^2}{n}$$

$$= \frac{(23)^2}{5} + \frac{(32)^2}{5} + \frac{(10)^2}{5} + \frac{(21)^2}{5} - 369.80$$

$$= 49.00$$

72

$$SS_w = SS_{tot} - SS_{bet}$$

$$= 100.20 - 49.00$$

$$= 51.20$$

$$s^2_{bet} = \frac{SS_{bet}}{df_{bet}} = \frac{49.00}{3} = 16.33$$

$$s^2_w = \frac{SS_w}{df_w} = \frac{51.20}{16} = 3.20$$

The results are summarized below:

ANOVA TABLE

Source of Variation	df	Sum of Squares	Variance Estimates
Between—group	3	49.00	16.33
Within—group	16	51.20	3.20
Total	19	100.20	

$$F = \frac{s^2_{bet}}{s^2_w} = \frac{16.33}{3.20} = 5.10, df = 3 \text{ and } 16$$

Since our obtained F = 5.10 exceeds the critical value (3.24), we reject H_o at $\alpha = 0.05$.

(b) In order to determine which conditions differ significantly, we employ Tukey's HSD test.

First, we set up a table of the differences among the means:

	$\overline{X}_1$	$\overline{X}_2$	$\overline{X}_3$	$\overline{X}_4$
$\overline{X}_1 = 4.6$	—	1.8	2.6	0.4
$\overline{X}_2 = 6.4$	—	—	4.4	2.2
$\overline{X}_3 = 2.0$	—	—	—	2.2
$\overline{X}_4 = 4.2$	—	—	—	—

A difference between two means is significant, at $\alpha = 0.01$, if it equals or exceeds HSD:

$$HSD = q\alpha \sqrt{\frac{s^2_w}{n}}$$

$$= 5.19 \sqrt{\frac{3.20}{5}}$$

$$= 4.15$$

According to this procedure, the only significant difference is the comparison $\overline{X}_2 - \overline{X}_3$.

2. a)

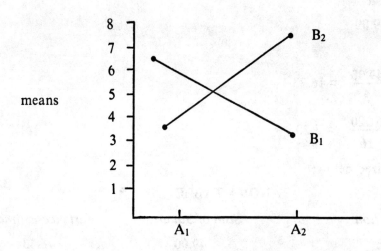

An interaction appears likely.

b) $SS_{tot} = 4^2 + 6^2 + 7^2 \ldots + 8^2 + 9^2 - \dfrac{(82)^2}{16}$

$= 494.00 - 420.25$

$= 73.75$

$SS_{bet} = \dfrac{(25)^2}{4} + \dfrac{(14)^2}{4} + \dfrac{(13)^2}{4} + \dfrac{(30)^2}{4} - 420.25$

$= 472.50 - 420.25$

$= 52.25$

$SS_w = SS_{tot} - SS_{bet}$

$= 73.75 - 52.25$

$= 21.50$

$SS_A = \dfrac{(39)^2}{8} + \dfrac{(43)^2}{8} - 420.25$

$= 421.25 - 420.25$

$= 1.00$

$SS_B = \dfrac{(38)^2}{8} + \dfrac{(44)^2}{8} - 420.25$

$= 422.50 - 420.25.$

$= 2.25$

$SS_{AxB} = SS_{bet} - SS_A - SS_B$

$= 52.25 - 1.00 - 2.25$

$= 49.00$

Variance estimates:

$$s^2_A = \frac{SS_A}{df_A} = \frac{1.00}{1} = 1.00$$

$$s^2_B = \frac{SS_B}{df_B} = \frac{2.25}{1} = 2.25$$

$$s^2_{AxB} = \frac{SS_{AxB}}{df_{AxB}} = \frac{49.00}{1} = 49.00$$

$$s^2_w = \frac{SS_w}{df_w} = \frac{21.50}{12} = 1.79$$

The results are summarized below:

ANOVA TABLE

Source of Variation	df	Sum of Squares	Variance Estimates
Between—group	3	52.25	
A—variable	1	1.00	1.00
B—variable	1	2.25	2.25
A x B	1	49.00	49.00
Within—group (error)	12	21.50	1.79
Total	15	73.75	

$$F = \frac{s^2_{AxB}}{s^2_w} = \frac{49.00}{1.79} = 27.37 \quad df = 1 \text{ and } 12$$

Employing $\alpha = 0.01$, an F-ratio of 9.33 or greater is required for significance for df = 1 and 12. The obtained F = 27.37 for the interaction is significant.

3. The various sums necessary for the calculations are:

Total $\quad \Sigma X_{tot} = 57 \quad \Sigma X^2_{tot} = 217 \quad \frac{(\Sigma X_{tot})^2}{n} = \frac{(57)^2}{18} = 180.5$

Blocks $\quad \Sigma X_{b_1} = 15 \quad \Sigma X_{b_2} = 12 \quad \Sigma X_{b_3} = 9 \quad \Sigma X_{b_4} = 6 \quad \Sigma X_{b_5} = 9 \quad \Sigma X_{b_6} = 6$

Treatments $\quad \Sigma X_{t_1} = 15 \quad \Sigma X_{t_2} = 18 \quad \Sigma X_{t_3} = 24$

$$SS_{tot} = \Sigma X^2_{tot} - \frac{(\Sigma X_{tot})^2}{n}$$

$$= 217 - 180.5$$

$$= 36.50$$

$$SS_{blks} = \frac{(\Sigma X_{b_1})^2 + (\Sigma X_{b_2})^2 + (\Sigma X_{b_3})^2 + (\Sigma X_{b_4})^2 + (\Sigma X_{b_5})^2 + (\Sigma_{b_6})^2}{n_{blk}} - 180.50$$

$$= \frac{(15)^2 + (12)^2 + (9)^2 + (6)^2 + (9)^2 + (6)^2}{3} - 180.50$$

$$= \frac{603}{3} - 180.50$$

$$= 20.50$$

$$SS_{treat} = \frac{(X_{t_1})^2 + (X_{t_2})^2 + (X_{t_3})^2}{n_{treat}} - 180.50$$

$$= \frac{(15)^2 + (18)^2 + (24)^2}{6} - 180.50$$

$$= 7.00$$

$$SS_w = SS_{tot} - SS_{blks} - SS_{treat}$$

$$= 36.50 - 20.50 - 7.00 = 9.00$$

Variance estimates

$$s^2_{blks} = \frac{SS_{blks}}{df_{blks}} = \frac{20.50}{5} = 4.10$$

$$s^2_{treat} = \frac{SS_{treat}}{df_{treat}} = \frac{7.00}{2} = 3.50$$

$$s^2_w = \frac{SS_w}{df_w} = \frac{9.00}{10} \quad 0.90$$

The results are summarized below:

ANOVA TABLE

Source	df	Sum of Squares	Variance Estimates
Blocks	5	20.50	4.10
Treatments	2	7.00	3.50
Error	10	9.00	0.90
Total	17	36.50	

$$F = \frac{s^2_{treat}}{s^2_w} = \frac{3.50}{0.90} = 3.89 \quad df = 2 \text{ and } 10$$

Using $\alpha = 0.05$ an F-ratio of 4.10 or greater is required for significance for df = 2 and 10. Since the obtained F = 3.89, we fail to reject H_o.

We may also test for the significance among the blocks:

$$F = \frac{4.10}{0.90} = 4.56 \quad df = 5 \text{ and } 10$$

Since our obtained F exceeds the critical value (3.33), we may conclude that blocking represents a significant source of variation.

Chapter 11

Chi Square and Nonparametric Tests of Significance

Lesson 11-1 Friedman Two-Way Analysis of Variance By Ranks

There are times when the data consist of ranks rather than quantitative values. Ranked data are often obtained when judgment rather than measurement is used. For example, when we judge a beauty contest or leadership qualities, we often rank one candidate against another. We usually assign a rank of 1 to the individual we judge highest in the quality assessed, a rank of 2 to the second, and so forth. Ranked data are not quantitative in the sense that equal differences are equal. Thus, the difference between the first and second candidates in a beauty contest is not equivalent to the difference between the second and third candidates. With quantitative variables, such as weight, we may claim that a difference of, say, one pound is the same throughout the scale of values.

Since the analysis of variance requires that the variable be quantitative, the procedures reviewed in Chapter 10 do not apply to ranked data. The Friedman two-way analysis by ranks is the ranked counterpart to the randomized block design. In the Friedman test, the columns represent the experimental conditions and the rows are the blocks. The data consist of ranks within blocks. For example, if there are four experimental conditions and ten blocks, ranks from 1 through 4 would be assigned within each block (row). When we sum the ranks on each column we may calculate the test statistic χ_r^2:

$$\chi_r^2 = \frac{12 \sum\limits_{i=1}^{k} (\Sigma R_i)^2}{nk(k+1)} - 3n(k+1)$$

where:

  n = the number of blocks (rows)

  k = the number of experimental conditions (columns)

ΣR_i = the sum of the ranks in the ith condition.

$\sum\limits_{i=1}^{k} (\Sigma R_i)^2$ direct us to sum the ranks in each condition, square these sums, and then sum these squares over the k conditions.

The null hypothesis assessed by the test is that all the experimental conditions (columns) are drawn from a common population; the table below provides exact probabilities when $k = 3$ and $n = 2$ through 9 and for $n = 2$ to 4 when k equals 4. For other values of n and k, the χ^2 table may be used in which $df = k-1$.

Probabilities associated with values as large as observed values of χ_r^2 in the Friedman two-way analysis of variance by ranks.

k = 3

n = 2		n = 3		n = 4		n = 5	
χ_r^2	p	χ_r^2	p	χ_r^2	p	χ_r^2	p
0	1.000	.000	1.000	.0	1.000	.0	1.000
1	.833	.667	.944	.5	.931	.4	.954
3	.500	2.000	.528	1.5	.653	1.2	.691
4	.167	2.667	.361	2.0	.431	1.6	.522
		4.667	.194	3.5	.273	2.8	.367
		6.000	.028	4.5	.125	3.6	.182
				6.0	.069	4.8	.124
				6.5	.042	5.2	.093
				8.0	.0046	6.4	.039
						7.6	.024
						8.4	.0085
						10.0	.00077

n = 6		n = 7		n = 8		n = 9	
χ_r^2	p	χ_r^2	p	χ_r^2	p	χ_r^2	p
.00	1.000	.000	1.000	.00	1.000	.000	1.000
.33	.956	.286	.964	.25	.967	.222	.971
1.00	.740	.857	.768	.75	.794	.667	.814
1.33	.570	1.143	.620	1.00	.654	.889	.865
2.33	.430	2.000	.486	1.75	.531	1.556	.569
3.00	.252	2.571	.305	2.25	.355	2.000	.398
4.00	.184	3.429	.237	3.00	.285	2.667	.328
4.33	.142	3.714	.192	3.25	.236	2.889	.278
5.33	.072	4.571	.112	4.00	.149	3.556	.187
6.33	.052	5.429	.085	4.75	.120	4.222	.154
7.00	.029	6.000	.052	5.25	.079	4.667	.107
8.33	.012	7.143	.027	6.25	.047	5.556	.069
9.00	.0081	7.714	.021	6.75	.038	6.000	.057
9.33	.0055	8.000	.016	7.00	.030	6.222	.048
10.33	.0017	8.857	.0084	7.75	.018	6.889	.031
12.00	.00013	10.286	.0036	9.00	.0099	8.000	.019
		10.571	.0027	9.25	.0080	8.222	.016
		11.143	.0012	9.75	.0048	8.667	.010
		12.286	.00032	10.75	.0024	9.556	.0060
		14.000	.000021	12.00	.0011	10.667	.0035
				12.25	.00086	10.889	.0029
				13.00	.00026	11.556	.0013
				14.25	.000061	12.667	.00066
				16.00	.0000036	13.556	.00035
						14.000	.00020
						14.222	.000097
						14.889	.000054
						16.222	.000011
						18.000	.0000006

$k = 4$

n = 2		n = 3		n = 4			
x_r^2	p	x_r^2	p	x_r^2	p	x_r^2	p
.0	1.000	.2	1.000	.0	1.000	5.7	.141
.6	.958	.6	.958	.3	.992	6.0	.105
1.2	.834	1.0	.910	.6	.928	6.3	.094
1.8	.792	1.8	.727	.9	.900	6.6	.077
2.4	.625	2.2	.608	1.2	.800	6.9	.068
3.0	.542	2.6	.524	1.5	.754	7.2	.054
3.6	.458	3.4	.446	1.8	.677	7.5	.052
4.2	.375	3.8	.342	2.1	.649	7.8	.036
4.8	.208	4.2	.300	2.4	.524	8.1	.033
5.4	.167	5.0	.207	2.7	.508	8.4	.019
6.0	.042	5.4	.175	3.0	.432	8.7	.014
		5.8	.148	3.3	.389	9.3	.012
		6.6	.075	3.6	.355	9.6	.0069
		7.0	.054	3.9	.324	9.9	.0062
		7.4	.033	4.5	.242	10.2	.0027
		8.2	.017	4.8	.200	10.8	0016
		9.0	.0017	5.1	.190	11.1	.00094
				5.4	.158	12.0	000072

Source: S. Siegel, *Nonparametric Statistics for the Behavioral Sciences.* New York: McGraw-Hill 1956. M. Friedman, The use of ranks to avoid the assumption of normality implicit in the analysis of variance. *F. Amer. Statist. Assn.,* **32**, 688-689, 1937.

Example: A firm wishes to offer a training program in leadership to their junior executives. Four different approaches to training are under consideration. To evaluate their effectiveness, 32 employees are randomly selected for participation in the study. Based on personnel records, they are divided into 8 groups of 4 each in which the members of each set of four are considered well matched in leadership qualities. These constitute the blocks. Each member of each block is randomly assigned to one of the four experimental conditions. Following training, their leadership qualities are assessed in a series of situations that demand the assertion of leadership. Each subject was rated in leadership by judges who were unaware of the conditions under which they were trained. The results were as follows:

Rank

Block	X_1	X_2	X_3	X_4
1	2	3	1	4
2	4	2	1	3
3	4	3	1	2
4	2	4	1	4
6	2	3	1	4
7	1	3	2	4
8	3	2	1	4
	$\Sigma R_1 = 20$	$\Sigma R_2 = 23$	$\Sigma R_1 = 9$	$\Sigma R_4 = 28$

Thus, we find:

$$\Sigma R_1 = 20 \qquad\qquad (\Sigma R_1)^2 = 400$$
$$\Sigma R_2 = 23 \qquad\qquad (\Sigma R_2)^2 = 529$$
$$\Sigma R_3 = 9 \qquad\qquad (\Sigma R_3)^2 = 81$$
$$\Sigma R_4 = 28 \qquad\qquad (\Sigma R_4)^2 = 784$$

To check the accuracy of the calculation, the sum of the ranks should equal:

$$n\left[\frac{k}{2}(k+1)\right]$$

In the present example:

$$8(2)(5) = 80$$

$$\Sigma R_1 + \Sigma R_2 + \Sigma R_3 + \Sigma R_4 = 80$$

We then substitute in the formula for χ_r^2 and solve:

$$\chi_r^2 = \frac{12 \sum_{i=1}^{k} (\Sigma R_i)^2 - 3n(k+1)}{nk(k+1)}$$

$$= \frac{12(400+529+81+784)}{(8)(4)(5)} - (3)(8)(5)$$

$$= 134.55 - 120$$

$$= 14.55$$

The critical value of χ^2 required for significance at $\alpha = 0.01$ is 11.341. Since obtained χ_r^2 exceeds this value, we may conclude that the various experimental conditions produced different ratings of leadership.

Multiple-Choice Items

1. To test the goodness of fit when more than two categories are involved, we could make use of: a) the binomial distribution; b) the multinomial distribution; c) the student t-ratio; d) none of the above.

2. When df = 1: a) $\chi^2 = z^2$; b) 68% of χ^2 values are between 0 and 1; c) χ^2 is skewed to the right; d) all of the above.

3. If n = 30, and there are three independent linear restrictions, df equals: a) 27; b) 33; c) 30; d) 29.

4. As df increases, the distributions of χ^2: a) become positively skewed; b) become negatively skewed; c) approach the form of the normal distribution; d) do not change.

5. If the critical value of χ^2 at $\alpha = 0.01$ is 21.666 and is 16.919 at $\alpha = 0.05$ and you obtain $\chi^2 = 17.204$: a) you would reject H_o at both α - levels; b) you would reject H_o at $\alpha = 0.01$ and fail to reject at $\alpha = 0.05$; c) you would fail to reject H_o at both levels of α; d) you would reject H_o at $\alpha = 0.05$ and fail to reject at $\alpha = 0.01$.

6. The ideal distribution for estimating probabilities when the variable is discrete and distributed over space and time is: a) χ^2; b) binomial; c) Poisson; d) normal.

7. To test for the independence of two categorical variables, we should use the _____ distribution: a) χ^2; b) binomial; c) Poisson; d) normal.

8. When using the sign test: a) we use the binomial when n is small (i.e., $n \leqslant 30$); b) we use the normal approximation to the binomial when n is large (n > 30); c) both a and b; d) none of the above.

9. If we wish to compare two independent samples that involve ranked data, the appropriate nonparametric test is: a) Mann-Whitney U; b) the sign test; c) the median test; d) the binomial test.

10. To test for the normality of a sequence, you should use: a) the binomial; b) the Poisson; c) χ^2; d) the median test.

11. To test for the randomness of a sequence, you should use: a) the normal probability distribution; b) Poisson; c) the binomial; d) the runs test.

12. In a 2x2 contingency table, the obtain frequency for each cell is 25. The n is equal to 100. The expected frequency for column 2 row 1 is: a) 50; b) 100; c) 25; d) 33.33.

13. In a 4x3 chi square test, the number of degrees of freedom is: a) 1; b) 12; c) 9; d) 6.

14. In testing H_o that p = ½ for a two-category population when n = 15, we should use: a) the binomial table for P = 0.50; b) the normal approximation to the binomial; c) the χ^2 test of independent; d) the Poisson approximation to binomial values.

15. The approximation of the binomial to the normal distribution is greatest when: a) n is small and P = 0.50; b) n is large and P $<$ 0.50; c) n is large and P $>$ 0.50; d) n is large and P = 0.50.

16. Given

$$p(x) = \frac{n!}{x!(n-x)!} \; P^x Q^{n-x}, \; n = 4, \; x = 3, \; P = ½, \; Q = ½,$$

the probability of x objects in the P category is: a) 0.25; b) 0.0625; c) 0.75; d) none of the above.

17. Given: $n_1 = 8$, $n_2 = 11$, $\alpha = 0.05$, two-tailed test, and the critical value of U is 23 or 65, we obtain a U of 21. We should: a) assert H_1; b) fail to reject H_o; c) assert H_o; d) none of the above.

18. A test of significance that uses the binomial as a sampling distribution is: a) the Mann-Whitney U; b) the runs test; c) the sign test; d) none of the above.

19. An alternative to the student t-ratio or the z-statistic when one wishes to avoid the assumptions of the parametric counterpart is: a) the sign test; b) the median test; c) the binomial test; d) the Mann-Whitney U.

Answers: 1. b; 2.d; 3. a; 4. c; 5. d; 6. c; 7. a; 8. c; 9. a; 10. c; 11. d; 12. c; 13. d; 14. a; 15. d; 16. a; 17. a; 18. c; 19. d.

Exercises

1. The chairperson of the economics department was interested in determining whether males or females differ in their preference for a male or female instructor. She randomly selected 100 male students and 100 female students and obtained the following results:

	Instructor	
	Male	*Female*
Male	40	60
Student		
Female	55	45

Using $\alpha = 0.01$, test H_o that the propotion of students favoring male or female instructors is independent of the gender of the student.

2. An independent research firm selects three random and independent samples of 40 people each. Of the 40 people using toothpaste A, 22 have no cavities. Of the 40 people using brand B, 18 have no cavities, and 26 of the 40 people using brand C have no cavitities. Employing $\alpha = 0.05$, what do you conclude?

3. The president of the local union was interested in determining the relationship, for union members, between years of employment and feelings about a particular issue. He surveyed 300 employees and obtained the following results. Employing $\alpha = 0.05$, what do you conclude?

Years of Employment	In Favor	Against
0—under 2	50	25
2—under 5	45	30
5—under 10	40	35
more than 10	35	40

4. The performance of 12 students was evaluated by judges before and after a special training session. The results are presented below:

Student	Before	After
1	C	C+
2	B-	A-
3	C+	A-
4	B-	B
5	B	B
6	B	B-
7	A-	B
8	C-	D
9	C-	C+
10	B-	B
11	A	A-
12	C	B-

Using $\alpha = 0.01$, what do you conclude?

5. A building contractor asked his two construction supervisors to rate 11 subcontractors on their reliability and workmanship. The ratings were from 1 to 10 where 10 was the poorest rating. Using $\alpha = 0.05$, determine whether thre is a significant difference in the ratings of the two supervisors.

Subcontractor	Supervisor I	Supervisor II
1	7	6
2	9	7
3	7	5
4	7	9
5	10	9
6	6	8
7	7	7
8	9	9
9	7	6
10	10	9
11	9	8

6. Suppose we conducted a study to determine the effects of training on reading speed. One group of 10 students is trained for 7 days; the other group of 9 subjects serves as a control group with no training.

The number of minutes required by each subject to read the test material is presented below:

Trained group	Control group
5.25	10
8.5	12.5
6.25	9
5	12
7.5	9
10.5	7.5
5.5	6
6.5	8
5.5	7
9.5	

82

Using $\alpha = 0.05$, what do you conclude?

7. A hearing aid distributor has been using a new supplier. Of 20 units returned for servicing, he finds they arrive in the following order (L= left, R= right):

L,L,L,R,L,L,R,R,R,R,R,L,L,L,L,R,R,R,R,R

Use $\alpha = 0.05$ and determine whether these data follow a random sequence.

8. An egg carton manufacturer inserts one of two types of advertising material into the cartons. The advertisers want randomness so that every consumer doesn't get the same ad. An independent testing company selects samples of 50 boxes to see if there is a proper mix of the two types of ads. They obtain the following:

1,2,1,1,1,2,2,2,1,1,2,1,1,1,1,2,2,2,2,1,2,2,1,1,1,2,2,2,2,2,1,1,1,2,2,1,1,1,2,1,1,2,2,2,1,1,2,2,2,2

Using $\alpha = 0.05$, test whether the advertisements are randomly mixed.

Answers

1. *Chi-square*

Instructor

		Male		Female		
		fo	fe	fo	fe	
	Male	40	47.5	60	52.5	100
Student						
	Female	55	47.5	45	52.5	100
		95		105		200

$$\chi = \frac{(40-47.5)^2}{47.5} + \frac{(55-47.5)^2}{47.5} + \frac{(60-52.5)^2}{52.5} + \frac{(45-52.5)^2}{52.5}$$

$$= 1.184 + 1.184 + 1.071 + 1.071$$

$$= 4.510$$

df = 1, critcal value at $\alpha = 01$ is 6.635.

We fail to reject H_o.

2.

		Brand A		Brand B		Brand C		
		fo	fe	fo	fe	fo	fe	
Cavities								
	Yes	18	18	22	18	14	18	54
	No	22	22	18	22	26	22	66
		40		40		40		120

$$\chi^2 = \frac{(18-18)^2}{18} + \frac{(22-22)^2}{22} + \frac{(22-18)^2}{18} + \frac{(18-22)^2}{22} + \frac{(14-18)^2}{18} + \frac{(26-22)^2}{22}$$

$$= 0 + 0 + 0.889 + 0.727 + 0.889 + 0.727$$

$$= 3.232$$

df = 2, critical value at $\alpha = 0.05$ is 5.991.

We fail to reject H_o.

3.

Years of Employment	In Favor		Against		
	fo	fe	fo	fe	
0—under 2	50	42.5	25	32.5	75
2—under 5	45	42.5	30	32.5	75
5—under 10	40	42.5	35	32.5	75
more than 10	35	42.5	40	32.5	75
	170		130		300

$$\chi^2 = \frac{(50-42.5)^2 + (45-42.5)^2 + (40-42.5)^2 + (35-42.5)^2}{42.5} +$$

$$\frac{(25-32.5)^2 + (30-32.5)^2 + (35-32.5)^2 + (40-32.5)^2}{32.5}$$

$$= 2.941 + 3.846$$

$$= 6.787$$

df = 3, critical value at α = 0.05 is 7.815.

We fail to reject H_o.

4. *Sign test*

Student	Before	After	Sign
1	C	C+	-
2	B-	A-	-
3	C+	A-	-
4	B-	B	-
5	B	B	0
6	B	B-	+
7	A-	B	+
8	C-	D	+
9	C-	C+	-
10	B-	B+	-
11	A	A-	+
12	C	B-	-

n = 11, x = 7, (p(x $\geq$ 7) = 0.2745. Accept H_o.

5. *Sign test*

n = 9, x = 7, p(x $\geq$ 7) = 0.0899. Accept H_o.

6. *Mann-Whitney U-test*

Trained Group	Rank	Control Group	Rank
5.25	2	10	16
8.5	12	12.5	19
6.25	6	9	13.5
5	1	12	18
7.5	9.5	9	13.5
10.5	17	7.5	9.5
5.5	3.5	6	5
6.5	7	8	11
5.5	3.5	7	8
9.5	15		
sums	76.5		113.5

$$U_1 = n_1 n_2 + \frac{n_1(n_1 + 1)}{2} - R_1$$

$$= 10(9) + \frac{10(11)}{2} - 76.5$$

$$= 68.5$$

$$U_2 = n_1 n_2 + \frac{n_2(n_2 + 1)}{2} - R_2$$

$$= 10(9) + \frac{9(10)}{2} - 113.5$$

$$= 21.5$$

For $\alpha = 0.05$ (two-tailed test), $n_1 = 10$, $n_2 = 9$, Table XI$_c$) U must be equal to or greater than 70 or equal to or less than 20 to be significant. Since our obtained statistics do not meet these requirements, we fail to reject H_o.

7. *Runs test* $n_L = 9$, $n_R = 11$, $R = 6$

   (Table XII). We reject H_o. The sequence is not random.

8. *Runs test* $n_1 = 24$, $n_2 = 26$, $R = 20$

$$\mu_R = \frac{2n_1 n_2}{n_1 + n_2} + 1 = \frac{2(24)(26)}{50} + 1$$

$$= 25.96$$

$$\sigma_R = \sqrt{\frac{2n_1 n_2 (2n_1 n_2 - n_1 n_2)}{(n_1 + n_2)^2 (n_1 + n_2 + 1)}} = \sqrt{\frac{2(24)(26)[2(24)(26) - 24 - 26]}{(50)^2 (51)}}$$

$$\sigma_R = \sqrt{\frac{1,495,104}{127,500}}$$

$$= 3.42$$

$25.96 \pm 1.96 (3.42)$

$19.26 - 32.66$

Since $R = 20$ lies within this interval, we fail to reject H_o.

Chapter 12

Linear Regression and Correlation

Lesson 12-1 Correlation and Causation

In Chapter 11 of the *Study Guide*, we noted that a true experiment is characterized by random assignment of subjects, objects, or events to experimental conditions and active manipulation of these conditions by the researcher. These procedures permit us to draw strong conclusions when H_o is rejected, vz., the manipulation of the independent variable *caused* the variation in the dependent variable. We also noted that many research studies mimic a true experiment but, lacking either random assignment and/or manipulation, they do not permit strong conclusions to be drawn.

Regression and correlational studies are a case in point. Since we relate the variables to one another after the fact, we cannot be sure that some other variables are not causing the regression between the independent and dependent variables. The following excerpt illustrates the difficulty in drawing strong conclusions from correlational data.

> We have all heard that a regular routine of exercise is related to physical well-being. Being a tennis fiend, I am quite comfortable with this conclusion. It seems obvious that any well-planned and regularly practiced physical fitness program must be salubrious. This includes jogging, if we overlook the greater incidence of jogger's toe, jobber's heel, jogger's arch, jogger's ankle, jogger's knee, and jogger's emphysema, to name but a few. The folk wisdom "Sound body, sound mind" is also appealing. But what causes what? Are active people more healthy because they are more active? Or are healthy people more likely to lead active physical lives because their good health enables them to do so? These questions simply cannot be answered on the basis of correlations. Incidentally, the health and medical sciences abound in "causal facts" that are really statements of relationships among variables.

> Now let's take a look at another popular conclusion. The figure graphs the anticipated lifetime income for male wage earners 25 years old and over who have enjoyed varying numbers of years of education. The earning power of education appears most impressive. Men with four or more years of college can expect to earn, over a lifetime, about three times as much money as those who failed to complete elementary school. Surely there is no better evidence that education is a sound economic investment. Right? Nonsense. Don't get me wrong. I have nothing against education. It has kept many pairs of shoes on the feet of my children over the years. Nor will I argue with the view that education provides many nonmonetary values that one may cherish often between matriculation and Medicare. In fact, I shall gladly assert the latter view. I still ruminate over outstanding lectures on philosophy, ethics, and psychology that I heard over 30 years ago during my undergraduate years. From my view, the value of education need not and should not be measured by an economic yardstick.

> But many people do. Their arguments go like this: "Look, if you don't get a college degree, you'll always be a schlep like Joe Snopes. You wanna be a schlep all your life? Not able to provide for your family? Welfare? Or do you want to be like Stan Upright. He's got a good college education and he's going places, let me tell you that."

> The only trouble is that the data do not prove that education leads to or causes higher incomes. The data merely prove that education people earn more. They may be economically successful for many reasons: They may be brighter or more highly motivated; they may be consummate con artists; they may have well-to-do parents or grandparents (a Rockefeller is likely to earn a healthy income during the course of a lifetime if he or she possesses no other skill than the ability to clip coupons from municipal bonds). Contrary to the view propaged in *The Wizard of Oz*, giving a college degree to a

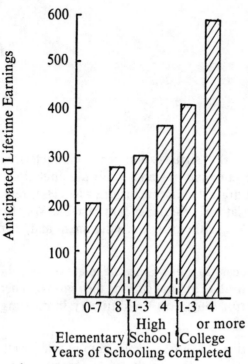

Lifetime Earnings. Expected lifetime earnings of male wage earners 25 years and older. Over a lifetime, a college graduate can expect to earn about three times as much as a male who never completed elementary school. (**Source:** U.S. Bureau of the Census. Series P-60, No. 74)

tin-head will not suddenly transform him into a computer capable of talking algebra. Stated succinctly, people who are educated differ in many ways from those who are not. Their economic success may stem from any one or a combination of all the ways in which they differ. It is no more appropriate to single out and credit education for the economic success of its graduates than it is to blame all of society's ills, as some do, on progressive trends in education of the "new math." (They learn that four plus two is equivalent to two plus four but do not know that either equals six.)

But that's not all. Take another look at the figure. Do you think that each of the columns is representative of the same population of wage earners with respect to all important variables? In this day of compulsory education, what age group is most likely to have failed to finish elementary school? Youngsters, middle-agers, or those breathing hard on FICA? Clearly, the last of the three. But they earned most of these wages prior to double-digit inflation, at a time when, as they saying goes, a dollar was worth a dollar. I even remember when 25 dollars a week was considered a living wage. Such citizens could not be expected to earn a whole lot of money over a lifetime, no matter how much education they had.

Now let's look at the right-hand column of the graph. What proportion of our older citizens obtained college degrees? Very few, I assure you. To be more precise, about 3 out of every 10,000 U.S. citizens graduated from college during the year 1900. In contrast, about 5 in every 1,000 graduated in 1977. Relative to their number, about 17 times as many great-grandchildren graduated from college as their great-grandparents.

So there you have it. Wage earners with low educational profiles are made up largely of older citizens who earned most of their income when wages were low. In contrast, those with high educational achievements are largely of the present generation, drawing income when wages are high. Their lifetime expectations are correspondingly high. So let's not justify education on pecuniary grounds. It simply doesn't wash.

How Numbers Lie (Runyon, 1981, pp. 133-36).

Multiple-Choice Items

1. The relationship between the area of a circle and the radius is: a) high and positive; b) low and negative; c) high and negative; d) completely determined.

Items 2-5 are based on the following graphs.

2. A positive relationship is depicted in: a) Figure A; b) Figure B; c) Figure C; d) Figure D.

3. A zero or low relationship is depicted in: a) Figure A; b) Figure B; c) Figure C; d) Figure D.

4. A curvilinear relationship is depicted in: a) Figure A; b) Figure B; c) Figure C; d) Figure D.

5. A negative relationship is depicted in: a) Figure A; b) Figure B; c) Figure C; d) Figure D.

6. Finding a regression equation that relates a predictor variable to a dependent variable: a) may be useful to predict future values of a dependent variable; b) may permit the predictor variable to be substituted for the dependent measure, saving time and money; c) may suggest a possible causal relationship; d) all of the above.

7.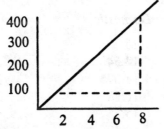

   The slope of the line is approximately: a) 50; b) 1.00; c) 0.50; d) 0.02.

8. In item 7, the Y intercept, a, is approximately: a) 100; b) 2; c) 0; d) 400.

9. In regression analysis: a) the independent variable is random; b) the dependent variable is random; c) both variables are random; d) both variables are fixed.

10. For any given value of X, the estimating equation predicts: a) the exact value of Y; b) the average value of Y over an entire data set; c) an average value of Y for a particular value of X; d) all of the above.

11. The Y intercept, a: a) often has no practical significance; b) is as important as the slope; c) shows the squared deviations of data points from the regression line; d) none of the above.

12. Homoscedasticity refers to: a) the conditional distributions of the Y variable; b) the scatter or variability of each conditional distribution; c) the standard deviations of each conditional distribution; d) all of the above.

13. The standard error or estimate: a) provides an estimate of the amount of scatter in the population; b) loses two degrees of freedom when using sample data to estimate A and B in the regression equation; c) may be interpreted like a standard deviation; d) all of the above.

14. The predictive intervals for individual forecasts are _____ than are those obtained for the conditional mean: a) wider; b) about the same; c) narrower; d) depends on the type of data.

15. In the absence of any information on X, our best prediction for Y would be: a) $\bar{Y}$; b) the conditional mean of Y for a given value of X; c) the mode of Y; d) none of the above.

16. The coefficient of determination is a ratio of: a) explained variation to unexplained variation; b) unexplained variation to total variation; c) explained variation to total variation; d) unexplained variation to total variation.

17. The sum of squares of observed values around the sample mean defines: a) explained variation; b) total variation; c) unexplained variation; d) none of the above.

18. If explained variation equals total variation: a) the correlation is 0; b) the correlation is ± 1.00; c) the correlation is low but greater than zero; d) the correlation cannot be determined without more information.

19. If r = 0.80, then: a) approximately 90 percent of the variation has been explained; b) 80 percent of the variation has been explained; c) 64 percent of the variation has been explained; d) 20 percent of the variation has been explained.

20. If r = 0.25, then k^2 equals: a) 0.9375; b) 0.0625; c) 0.75; d) 0.50.

Answers: 1. d; 2. d; 3. a; 4. c; 5. b; 6. d; 7. a; 8. c; 9. b; 10. c; 11. a; 12. d; 13. d; 14. a; 15. a; 16. c; 17. b; 18. b; 19. c; 20. a

Exercises

1. The following data present the billions of dollars of revenue for air carriers' passenger-miles for domestic and international operations for 1979 and the first 11 months of 1980.

		X Domestic	Y International
1979	Jan.	15.22	3.90
	Feb.	14.54	3.05
	Mar.	18.37	3.76
	Apr.	16.28	3.99
	May	15.75	4.32
	June	18.32	5.15
	July	19.71	5.75
	Aug.	21.30	6.02
	Sept.	15.72	4.90
	Oct.	16.48	4.40
	Nov.	15.85	3.73
	Dec.	16.50	4.00

		X Domestic	Y International
1980	Jan.	15.87	4.12
	Feb.	15.14	3.43
	Mar.	18.01	4.05
	Apr.	16.48	4.04
	May	16.06	4.52
	June	18.19	5.08
	July	18.64	5.85
	Aug.	20.25	6.76
	Sept.	14.84	4.77
	Oct.	15.80	4.25
	Nov.	14.24	3.62

(2) Calculate both a and b;

(b) Find the regression equation.

(c) Find Yc (international revenue) if X = 15; 17; 20.

(d) Find the 95 percent confidence interval for the mean international revenue for air carriers as a whole when domestic revenues are 18.5 billion.

(e) Find the coefficient of correlation.

(f) What proportion of variation in Y can be explained by variations in domestic revenues?

2. The following data present the production of beer (in millions of barrels) and the production of effervescent wines (in millions of wine gallons) for 1979 and the first 11 months of 1980.

		Beer	Wine
1979	Jan.	13.83	1.93
	Feb.	13.57	1.66
	Mar.	16.89	1.80
	Apr.	16.34	1.91
	May	16.97	2.49
	June	16.77	1.89
	July	16.94	1.58
	Aug.	16.76	2.25
	Sept.	14.70	2.03
	Oct.	15.28	2.84
	Nov.	13.14	1.47
	Dec.	12.18	1.59
1980	Jan.	14.64	1.62
	Feb.	14.72	1.47
	Mar.	16.56	1.80
	Apr.	16.36	1.72
	May	17.97	2.21
	June	17.93	1.62
	July	18.72	1.98
	Aug.	17.02	2.65
	Sept.	16.29	1.92
	Oct.	14.95	3.61
	Nov.	13.02	2.42

Exercise 2 is continued on the following page.

(a) Calculate both a and b.

(b) Find the regression equation.

(c) Find Yc (millions of wine gallons) if X = 14; 16; 18.

(d) Find the 95 percent confidence interval for mean wine production when beer production is 17 million barrels.

(e) Find the coefficient of correlation.

(f) What proportion of variation in Y can be explained by variations in beer production?

Answers

1.
		XY
1979	Jan.	59.3580
	Feb.	44.3470
	Mar.	69.0712
	Apr.	64.9572
	May	68.0400
	June	94.3480
	July	113.3325
	Aug.	128.2260
	Sept.	77.0280
	Oct.	72.5120
	Nov.	59.1205
	Dec.	66.0000
1980	Jan.	65.3844
	Feb.	51.9302
	Mar.	72.9405
	Apr.	66.5792
	May	72.5912
	June	92.4052
	July	109.0440
	Aug.	136.8900
	Sept.	70.7868
	Oct.	67.1500
	Nov.	51.5488

$\Sigma X = 387.86$

$\Sigma X^2 = 6618.3916$

$\overline{X} = 16.8635$

$\Sigma Y = 103.46$

$\Sigma Y^2 = 483.8810$

$\overline{Y} = 4.4983$

$n = 23$

$\Sigma XY = 1773.5907$

(a)
$$b = \frac{n(\Sigma XY) - (\Sigma X)(\Sigma Y)}{n(\Sigma X^2) - (\Sigma X)^2}$$

$$= \frac{23(1773.5907) - (387.86)(103.46)}{23(6618.3916) - (387.86)^2}$$

$$= \frac{664.5905}{1787.6272}$$

$$= 0.3718$$

$$a = \frac{\Sigma Y - b\Sigma X}{n}$$

$$= \frac{103.46 - (0.3718)(387.86)}{23}$$

$$= -1.7716$$

92

(b) $Y_c = a + bX$

$\quad\quad = -1.7716 + 0.3718\ X$

(c) $X = 15$ $\quad\quad\quad\quad\quad\quad\quad X = 17$ $\quad\quad\quad\quad\quad\quad\quad X = 20$

$\quad\ \ Y_c = 3.81$ $\quad\quad\quad\quad\quad\quad Y_c = 4.55$ $\quad\quad\quad\quad\quad\quad Y_c = 5.66$

(d) $\quad s_{y.x} = \sqrt{\dfrac{\Sigma Y^2 - a\Sigma Y - b\Sigma XY}{n-2}}$

$\quad\quad\quad\quad = \sqrt{\dfrac{483.8810 - (-1.7716)(103.46) - 0.3718\,(1773.5907)}{21}}$

$\quad\quad\quad\quad = 0.6075$

$\quad s_{yc} = s_{y.x}\sqrt{\dfrac{1}{n}\dfrac{(X-\bar{X})^2}{\Sigma X^2 - \dfrac{(\Sigma X)^2}{n}}}$

$\quad\quad\quad = 0.6075\sqrt{\dfrac{1}{23}\dfrac{(18.5-16.8635)^2}{6618.3916 - \dfrac{(387.86)^2}{23}}}$

$\quad\quad\quad = 0.0235$

$Y_c \pm t\ s_{yc}$ $\quad$ required t for df = n-2 at 0.95 confidence is 2.080

Y_c for X = 18.5

$Y_c = 5.1067$

$\quad\quad 5.1067 \pm 2.080\ (0.0235)$

$\quad\quad\quad\quad \pm 0.0489$

$\quad\quad 5.0578$ to 5.1556

(e)

$\quad r = \dfrac{\Sigma XY - \dfrac{(\Sigma X)(\Sigma Y)}{n}}{\sqrt{\left[\Sigma X^2 - \dfrac{-(\Sigma X)^2}{n}\right]\left[\Sigma Y^2 - \dfrac{(\Sigma Y)^2}{n}\right]}}$

$\quad\quad = \dfrac{1773.5907 - \dfrac{(387.86)\,(103.46)}{23}}{\sqrt{\left[6618.3916 - \dfrac{(387.86)^2}{23}\right]\left[483.8810 - \dfrac{(103.46)^2}{23}\right]}}$

$\quad\quad = \dfrac{28.8952}{37.9100} = 0.7622$

(f) $\quad r^2 = (0.7622)^2 = 0.5809$ or approximately 58%.

2.　$\Sigma XY = 716.0911$　　$\Sigma X = 361.55$　　$\Sigma Y = 46.46$

　　　　　　　　　　　　　$\Sigma X^2 = 5751.1397$　$\Sigma Y^2 = 99.5852$

　　　　　　　　　　　　　$\bar{X} = 15.7196$　　$\bar{Y} = 2.02$

(a)　$b = \dfrac{23(716.0911)-(361.55)(46.46)}{23(5751.1397) - (361.55)^2}$

　　　　$= \dfrac{-327.5177}{1557.8106}$

　　　　$= -0.02102$

　　$a = \dfrac{46.46-(-0.2102)(361.55)}{23}$

　　　　$= 5.3243$

(b)　$Y_c = 5.3243 - 0.2102\,X$

(c)　$X = 14$　　　　　　$X = 16$　　　　　　$X = 18$

　　　$Y_c = 2.38$　　　　$Y_c = 1.96$　　　　$Y_c = 1.54$

(d)　$s_{y.x} = \sqrt{\dfrac{99.5852 - 5.3243(46.46)-(-0.2102)(716.0911)}{21}}$

　　　　　$= 0.3613$

　　$s_{y_c} = 0.3613 \sqrt{\dfrac{1}{23}\;\dfrac{(17-15.7196)^2}{5751.1397- \dfrac{(361.55)^2}{23}}}$

　　　　　$= 0.2753$

$Y_c \pm t\, s_{yc}$

Y_c for $X = 17$ is 1.7509

$1.7509 \pm 2.080\,(0.2753)$

　　　　± 0.5726

1.1783 to 2.3235

(e)

$$r = \sqrt{\dfrac{716.0911 - \dfrac{(361.55)(46.46)}{23}}{\left[5751.1397 - \dfrac{(361.55)^2}{23}\right]\left[99.5852 - \dfrac{(46.46)^2}{23}\right]}}$$

　　$= \dfrac{-14.2399}{19.7105}$

　　$= -0.7225$

(f)　$r^2 = 0.5220$

Chapter 13

Multiple Regression Analysis

Lesson 13-1   Multiple Regression as an Alternative to ANOVA

In Chapter 10 of the text we described a powerful tool for designing and analyzing complex "experiments," viz., two variable factorial designs analyzed by the use of analyses of variance techniques. In Chapter 11 we noted that a true experiment permits strong conclusions (i.e., causality) because it uses random assignment and manipulation of the independent variable. In Chapter 12, we further observed that most regression and correlational studies do not permit strong conclusions to be drawn. This is due to the fact that most of these studies involve events or states of nature over which the researchers have no control. One cannot, for example, manipulate the prime rate to see what effect it has on stock market prices. Consequently, if a relationship is found, we cannot conclude that prime rate changes *cause* changes in prices of common stock. When prime rate goes up or down, there are many other factors in the economy that are also going up or down (including the mood and optimism of investors) any one or combination of which might affect stock prices.

When the independent variable can be manipulated (as in the gasoline additive example in the text), multiple regression analysis provides an alternative procedure to ANOVA. This is particularly the case when our objective is to achieve some practical goal (such as improving gasoline mileage) rather than deciding some theoretical issue. It is important, however, that the two independent variables not be correlated. To achieve this, the level of the independent variable could be randomly assigned to each person or object participating in the study. The resulting regression plane would permit us to answer, within limits, such questions as, "what would happen if we increased the level of X_1 by five and decrease the level of X_2 by three?" Moreover, these procedures would permit strong conclusions to be drawn concerning the effects of the independent variables.

Multiple-Choice Items

1. In multiple-regression analysis, there are _____ independent variables(s): a) one; b) two; c) three; d) more than one.

2. In multiple-regression analysis, the estimating equation for two variables is: a) a one-dimensional plane; b) a two-dimensional plane; c) a three-dimensional plane; d) multidimensional space.

3. The estimating equation for three independent variables is: a) $Y_c = a+bX$; b) $Y_c = a+b_1X_1b_2X_2$; c) $Y_c = a+b_1X_1+b_2X_2+b_3X_3$; d) none of the above.

4. In a multiple regression analysis using two independent variables, the number of degrees of freedom is: a) n-1; b) n-2; c) n-3; d) n-4.

5. The use of t and the standard error of estimate in multiple regression analysis assumes: a) scatter is normally distributed; b) for any values of X_1 and X_2, the standard deviations of the error are the same; c) both a and b; d) none of the above.

6. The coefficient of multiple determination shows: a) the proportion of total variation in Y that is accounted for by the regression plane; b) the proportion of total variation that is unexplained; c) the proportion of error variation that is unexplained; d) the proportion of error variation that is explained.

7. Given a = 20, b_1 = 0.32, and b_2 = 0.16, X_1 = 30, and X_2 = 40, Y_c equals: a) 37.6; b) 36; c) 20.48; d) 51.2.

8. Using the daily price of silver and gold as predictor variables in a multiple regression analysis: a) may be very revealing since both are so closely related; b) may lead to the problem of multicollinearity; c) may involve problems of serial correlation; d) will be most useful since their prices are probably independent.

9. If we encounter difficulties because the variables we are studying occur over the same time span, the problem is: a) serial correlation; b) multicollinearity; c) the error terms may be correlated; d) both a and c.

10. If $b_1 = 0.70$ and $b_2 = -0.30$, increasing values of X_2 while holding values of X_1 constant will: a) increase values of Y_c; b) decrease values of Y_c; c) maintain values of Y_c constant; d) depends on the value of the Y intercept 0.

Answers: 1. d; 2. c; 3. c; 4. c; 5. c; 6. a; 7. b; 8. b; 9. d; 10. b

Exercises

The president of the Association of Health Care Facilities wishes to learn the relationship between age, marital status, years of experience, and number of job changes for nurses. Randomly selecting 75 different nurses, the following computer output was obtained:

VARIABLES IN THE EQUATION

VARIABLE	COEFFICIENT	STD. ERROR	T-VALUE
Age 1	-1.06345	0.30241	3.51658
Mar 2	0.07194	0.06812	1.05608
Years 3	0.16012	0.09433	1.69745
(Constant)	2.18321		

ANALYSIS OF VARIANCE	DF	SUM OF SQUARES	MEAN SQUARE	F
REGRESSION	3	20.06214	6.68738	44.10037
RESIDUAL	71	10.76674	0.15164	

Multiple R 0.87437
R SQUARE 0.76452
STD. ERROR OF EST. 0.63448

(a) Write the multiple regression equation for predicting number of job changes from the three independent variables.

(b) Using $\alpha = 0.05$, test the null hypothesis that the population coefficients are zero

(c) Using $\alpha = 0.05$, test the null hypothesis that population $R^2 = 0$.

(d) Interpret the results.

Answers

(a) $Y_c = 2.18321 - 1.06345 X_1 + 0.07194 X_2 + 0.16012 X_3$

(b) df = 73, for "age," we reject H_o. For martial status and years of experience, we fail to reject H_o.

(c) F = 44.10037 exceeds the critical value for $\alpha = 0.05$, df = 3, 71.

(d) Approximately 76 percent of the variance is accounted for by the multiple regression of age, marital status, and years of experience. If marital status and years of experience is held constant, increasing age leads to few job changes.

If age and years of experience is held constant, and 1 = married, 2 = not married, married nurses change jobs less often. If age and marital status is held constant, increasing years of experience leads to increasing number of job changes.

Caution: We are NOT saying that these independent variables *cause* job changes.

"I wish you had come to me sooner."

Lesson 14-1 Additive and Mixed Model Time Series

In the text, we pointed out the fact that the following is the most common time series model:

$$Y = T \times C \times S \times I.$$

This model assumes that the components act in combination to produce the time series. Its popularity stems from the fact that this model is particularly adapted to situations in which the *percentage of change* best reflects the movement in the series. It so happens that much business and economic data are best summarized by percentage of change. Hence the widespread use of the multiplicative model.

Any given time series may be better represented by some other model. For some the additive model may be appropriate. This model may be represented by the following:

$$Y = T + C + S + I.$$

At times, some components may interact in an additive fashion while others interact in a multiplicative manner. Under these circumstances, a mixed model may be most appropriate. Following are the mixed additive and multiplicative models of a time series:

$$Y = T \times C \times S + I$$
$$Y = T \times C + S \times I$$
$$Y = T + C \times S \times I$$
$$Y = T \times C + S + I$$
$$Y = T + C \times S + I$$
$$Y = T + C + S \times I$$

Lesson 14-2 Exponential Growth

In the text, we pointed out that exponential curves increase or decrease by a constant rate from time period to time period. If you ignore the timespan, increasing exponential curves are like bombs that appear to burst forth all at once. The following excerpt from *How Numbers Lie* (Runyon, 1981, pp. 59-63) provides an amusing example of "how exponential growth can sneak up on you."

Extrapolating Exponential Growth

I am sure you have heard this puzzler. A single water hyacinth is placed in a pond. Each day the number doubles so that at the end of twenty days the entire surface of the pond is covered. How long do the hyacinths take to occupy one half of the pond's surface?

Our first tendency is to blurt out "ten days." This is due to the fact much of the arithmetic of daily living involves straight-line relationships. Of we are paid $8 an hour, we can determine how much we are owed merely by multiplying $8 by the number of hours worked. Thus, we we work ten hours, we are owed $80. If we rent an apartment for $600 per month, we can calculate our daily rate merely dividing by the number of days in a month. If there are thirty days, the daily rate is $20. But anyone familiar with water hyacinths knows that they do not propagate in a straight-line fashion. Rather, their reproduction is more like an explosion in slow motion. One day there is one; the next day there's two; the next day, four; the succeeding day, eight; and so forth. Why, last summer I introduced two into a fish pond with approximately 200 square feet of surface. Within less than a month, the entire surface was cluttered with hyacinths.

The answer to the puzzle? Why, nineteen days, of course. If the number of plants doubles each day, then on the twentieth day the number is double that of the nineteenth day. Consequently, compared to day twenty there are half as many hyacinths in the pond on day nineteen. In fact, there were only one-quarter as many on day eighteen, one-eighth as many on day seventeen, and so forth.

Here's another one you have surely heard. A down-and-out baseball player went to a big-league manager at the beginning of spring training. Joe Aintgotit explained his burning desire to make the big time and offered a contract his manager couldn't refuse. "I'll play for a penny the first day, two pennies the second day. I only ask that you double my salary each day for thirty days. In other words, I want only a 30-day no-cut clause in which I am willing to give my all for just pennies a day. In fact, you may dispense with the usual room-and-board allowance. That's how much an opportunity to make the team means to me. At the end of thirty days, we can negotiate the contract, if you feel I've got what it takes."

The manager happily signed the contract. He was ecstatic at the unprecedented opportunity to get a "free" look at a highly motivated athlete. Only, much to his chagrin, he discovererd that his perfect "deal" involved a somewhat greater financial risk than he had bargained for. To be more precise, he paid out $5,368,709.12 on the thirtieth day; $2,684,354.56 on the twenty-ninth day; $1,342,177.28 on the twenty-eighth day; etc. Naturally, the manager was fired by his new owner—Joe Aintgotit, who, sad to relate, never made the club.

That's the main characteristic of types of growth that we call exponential. One day they are hardly discernible; the next day, month, year, they explode in your face. Some everyday phenomena that pursue roughly exponential growth rates are population, compound interest, consumption of resources, and development of new industries (e.g., petroleum, auto, plastics, computers).

The fun comes when we attempt to extrapolate these growth rates to make precise projections about the future. There's a little trick in making these projections that everyone should master. If you know the rate of compound interest, you divide that into 70 and obtain a rough approximation of the doubling time. Let's look at a few examples.

- At the age of 30, you deposit $1,000 in a savings bond that provides 10 percent annual rate of interest. Assuming that the bond is indefinitely renewable at the same rate of interest, how old would you be before you doubled your savings? Well, seventy divided by 10 is 7. Seven years is the doubling time. Thus, by age 37, you would be the proud possessor of a bond worth $2,000. By 44, it would be worth $4,000; $8,000 by the age of 51. "What's that question? How much would be in that account by the time you reached the century mark in age? That's easy. Almost a million bucks. Why that dour look? Don't think you'll make it to a hundred? Oh, it's not that at all? Oh, I see, you're afraid inflation will take the edge off being a millionaire."

- For a decade prior to 1970, the energy growth rate in the United States was about 7 percent per year. Based on that rate, the doubling time in energy use would be about ten years; the quadrupling time would be about twenty years. In *The Energy Crisis,* Dr. Rocks and I suggested that by the turn of the century we could be using *eight* times as much energy as in 1970. Inveterate hedgers that we are, we followed up this starting projection with the disclaimer, "Obviously, this compounded rate can't be maintained indefinitely."[1] Indeed, it has not. Thanks largely to the Organization of Petroleum Exporting Countries and declining oil reserves in this country, the rate of increase in energy use has dropped sharply. It is now less than 2 percent per year, compounded. At the present rate, we would estimate the quadrupling time as seventy or more years in the future. How fragile are predictions from unstable growth rates!

Of course, they must be. The ready availability and accessibility of an important resource invites its exploitation as rapidly as possible. But then less becomes available. What is available becomes less accessible, and the compounded growth rate is sharply curtailed. The $64,000 question then becomes, "Will we find viable alternatives to head off the inevitable social, political, financial, and personal upheaval that must follow a failure to do so?" Although I cannot prove it, I have a hunch that many advanced civilizations that have mysteriously disappeared in the past have done so because they exhausted some key elements for which they could find no alternatives. Thought for the day: Will energy be our Achilles' heel?

[1] Rocks, L. and R. P. Runyon, *The Energy Crisis*, 1972 (Crown, p. 10).

Multiple-Choice Items

1. For fairly long-range forecasts, we examine: a) trend; b) seasonal fluctuations; c) irregular fluctuations; d) positive slopes.

2. Ups and downs around forecast lines observed over long periods of time refer to: a) trend; b) cyclical fluctuations; c) seasonal fluctuations; d) irregular fluctuations.

3. Fluctuations that are erratic and of short duration are known as: a) trend; b) cyclical fluctuations; c) seasonal fluctuations; d) irregular fluctuations.

4. Patterns that occur during a year and tend to repeat themselves each year refer to: a) trend; b) cyclical fluctuations; c) seasonal fluctuations; d) irregular fluctuations.

5. The most common time series model is represented by:

   a) $Y = T + C + S + I$; b) $Y = T \times C \times S + I$; c) $Y = T + C \times S \times I$; d) $Y = T \times C \times S \times I$.

6. When dealing with annual data, deviations from a linear trend line: a) represent cyclical and regular fluctuations; b) represent seasonal variations; c) are considered random; d) represent cyclical and irregular fluctuations.

7. A(n) _____ trend line increases or decreases at a constant *rate:* a) exponential; b) linear; c) parabolic; d) irregular.

8. When trends change direction, a(n) _____ trend line may be appropriate: a) exponential; b) linear; c) parabolic; d) irregular.

9. A constant *amount* of increase or decrease may best be described by a(n) _____ trend line. A) exponential; b) linear; c) parabolic; d) irregular.

Items 10-13 are based on the following diagram.

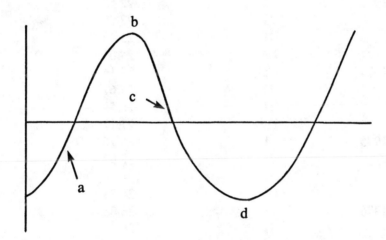

10. The phase of the business cycle shown by a is: a) peak; b) expansion; c) trough; d) recession.

11. The phase of the business cycle shown by b is: a) peak; b) expansion; c) trough; d) recession.

12. The phase of the business cycle shown by c is: a) peak; b) expansion; c) trough; d) recession.

13. The phase of the business cycle shown by d is: a) peak; b) expansion; c) trough; d) recession.

14. Using the multiplicative model, when we remove the trend and cyclic components, we are left with: a) $Y = T \times C$; b) $Y = C \times S$; c) $Y = C \times I$; d) $Y = S \times I$.

15. Variations that occur within a year are: a) seasonal; b) cyclic; c) trend; d) irregular.

16. The method of moving averages is used to eliminate the: a) seasonal elements; b) trend and cyclical elements; c) irregular elements; d) all of the above.

17. By dividing the data by the corresponding seasonal index and multiplying by 100, we have: a) deseasonalized the data; b) eliminated trend components; c) eliminated irregular elements; d) eliminated cyclic fluctuations.

18. There are three elements in a forecast. These are: a) uncertainty, a crystal ball, and time frame; b) certainty, dependence on historical records, time frame; c) uncertainty, dependence on historical records, time frame; d) uncertainty, an historical vacuum, time frame.

Answers: 1. a; 2. b; 3. d; 4. c; 5. d; 6. d; 7. a; 8. c; 9. b; 10. b; 11. a; 12. d; 13. c; 14. d; 15. a; 16. b; 17. a; 18. c.

Exercises

1. Suppose you knew that MAJ Bread Company regularly accounted for 0.005 percent of the total retail food sales in certain target areas. Could you use this information to project future sales for MAJ Bread Co.? What information would you need to make this forecast? What would you have to assume?

Answer

1. If you knew the total sales (or had a way to estimate them) for the time period of interest, you could multiply this total by 0.005 percent to estimate MAJ's future sales. You would have to assume that MAJ's history will be repeated in the future (i.e., that they represent 0.005 percent of the total market).

2. The following table presents quarterly sums of home mortgage rates for conventional first mortgages from 1973 to the third quarter of 1980.

	Quarter	Mortgage Rate Sums
1973	I	22.55
	II	22.70
	III	23.44
	IV	24.65
1974	I	25.16
	II	25.67
	III	26.59
	IV	27.12
1975	I	26.76
	II	26.07
	III	25.99
	IV	26.23
1976	I	26.05
	II	26.11
	III	26.40
	IV	26.55
1977	I	26.04
	II	26.25
	III	26.42
	IV	26.56
1978	I	26.92
	II	27.44
	III	28.29
	IV	28.99
1979	I	29.88
	II	30.65
	III	31.94
	IV	33.25
1980	I	35.33
	II	38.14
	III	35.88

(a) Calculate the moving averages.
(b) Graph the actual data against the moving average.
(c) Calculate the percent-of-moving average figures.
(d) Graph the percent-of-moving average figures.
(e) Calculate the quarterly seasonal indexes.
(f) Deseasonalize the data.
(g) Graph the deseasonalized data.
(h) Using the deseasonalized values, fit a parabolic trend line.
(i) Calculate each of the trend values.
(j) What do these trend values mean?
(k) Graph the trend line against the deseasonalized data.
(l) Divide each of the deseasonalized values by its corresponding trend value and multiply by 100. Graph the resulting figures and explain what is reflected by these figures.
(m) Predict the seasonally adjusted sum of mortgage rates for the fourth quarter of 1980 and the first quarter of 1981.

Answer
2.

Year	Quarter	Y Quarterly Sums	Four-Quarter Moving Total	Eight-Quarter Moving Total	(a) MA	(c) % MA $\frac{Y}{MA} \times 100$	SI	(f) Deseasonalized $\frac{Y}{SI} \times 100$
1973	I	22.55					100.1	22.53
	II	22.70					99.4	22.84
	III	23.44	93.34	189.29	23.66	99.07	100.0	23.44
	IV	24.65	95.95	194.87	24.36	101.19	100.6	24.50
1974	I	25.16	98.92	200.99	25.12	100.16	100.1	25.13
	II	25.67	102.07	206.61	25.83	99.38	99.4	25.82
	III	26.59	104.54	210.68	26.34	100.95	100.0	26.59
	IV	27.12	106.14	212.68	26.58	102.03	100.6	26.96
1975	I	26.76	106.54	212.48	26.56	100.75	100.1	26.73
	II	26.07	105.94	210.99	26.37	98.86	99.4	26.23
	III	25.99	105.05	209.39	26.17	99.31	100.0	25.99
	IV	26.23	104.34	208.72	26.09	100.54	100.6	26.07
1976	I	26.05	104.38	209.17	26.15	99.62	100.1	26.02
	II	26.11	104.79	209.90	26.24	99.35	99.4	26.27
	III	26.40	105.11	210.21	26.28	100.46	100.0	26.40
	IV	26.55	105.10	210.34	26.29	100.99	100.6	26.39
1977	I	26.04	105.24	210.50	26.31	98.97	100.1	26.01
	II	26.25	105.26	210.53	26.32	99.73	99.4	26.41
	III	26.42	105.27	211.42	26.43	99.96	100.0	26.42
	IV	26.56	106.15	213.49	26.69	99.51	100.6	26.40
1978	I	26.92	107.34	216.55	27.07	99.45	100.1	26.89
	II	27.44	109.21	220.85	27.61	99.38	99.4	27.61
	III	28.29	111.64	226.24	28.28	100.04	100.0	28.29
	IV	28.99	114.60	232.41	29.05	99.79	100.6	28.82
1979	I	29.88	117.81	239.27	29.91	99.90	110.1	29.85
	II	30.65	121.46	247.18	30.90	95.45	99.4	30.84
	III	31.94	125.72	256.89	32.11	99.47	100.0	31.94
	IV	33.25	131.17	269.83	33.73	98.58	100.6	33.05
1980	I	35.33	138.66	281.26	35.16	100.48	100.1	35.29
	II	38.14	142.60					
	III	35.88						

101

(b) Mortgage Rates Quarterly

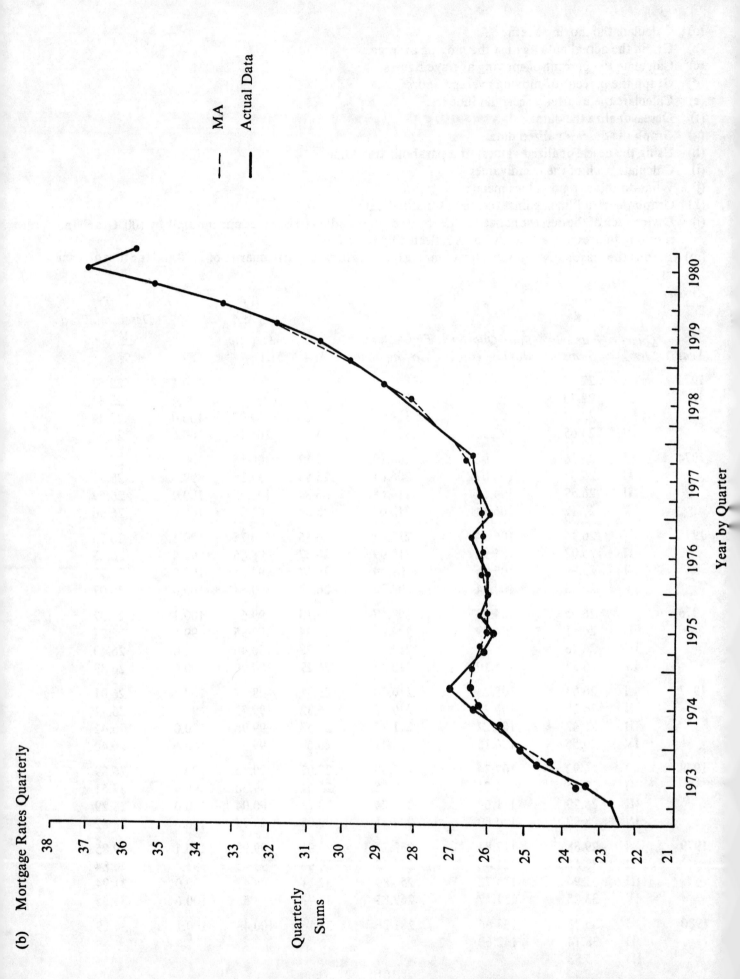

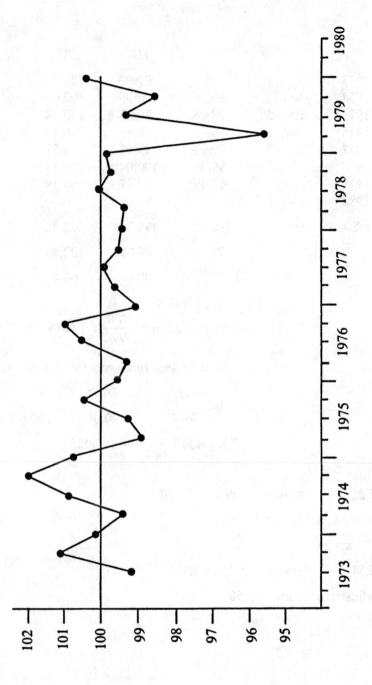

% MA

Seasonal Indexes
Mortgage Rates

(e)

	I	II	III	IV
1973			~~99.07~~	101.19
1974	100.16	99.38	~~100.95~~	~~102.03~~
1975	~~100.75~~	98.86	99.31	100.54
1976	99.62	99.35	100.46	100.99
1977	~~98.97~~	~~99.73~~	99.96	99.51
1978	99.45	99.38	100.04	99.79
1979	99.90	~~95.45~~	99.47	~~98.58~~
1980	100.48			
ΣX	499.61	396.97	499.24	502.02
$\overline{X}$	99.92	99.24	99.85	100.40
	99.9	99.2	99.8	100.4

$$\Sigma \overline{X} = 399.3$$

$$\text{Adjustment factor} = \frac{400}{399.3} = 1.0018$$

Seasonal Indexes

I	II	III	IV
100.1	99.4	100.0	100.6

$$\Sigma \overline{X} = 400.1 \qquad \overline{X} = 100.025$$

(m) 1980 IV $x = 17$,

$Y_t = 34.82$ seasonal index = 102.70

seasonally adjusted amount = 35.50

1981 I $x = 18$

$Y_t = 35.54$ seasonal index = 100.1

seasonally adjusted amount = 35.50

(g) and (k)

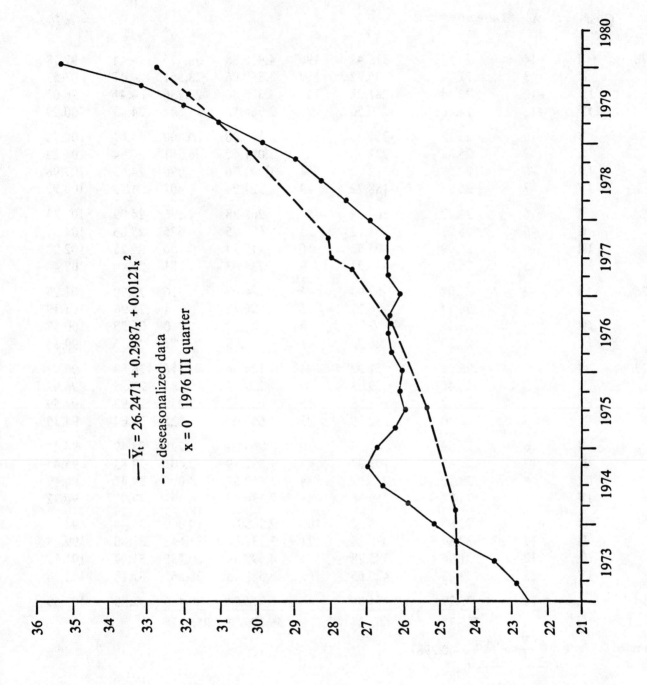

$\overline{Y}_t = 26.2471 + 0.2987x + 0.0121x^2$

--- deseasonalized data

x = 0   1976 III quarter

(h)   *Parabolic*

								(i)	(l)
Year	Quar-ter	$(X-\bar{X})$ x	Deseasonalized Y	xY	x^2	x^2Y	x^4	Y_t	$\dfrac{Y}{Y_t} \times 100$
1973	I	-14	22.53	-315.42	196	4,415.88	38,416	24.44	92.18
	II	-13	22.84	-296.92	169	3,859.96	28,561	24.41	93.57
	III	-12	23.44	-281.28	144	3,375.36	20,736	24.41	96.03
	IV	-11	24.50	-269.50	121	2,964.50	14,641	24.43	100.29
1974	I	-10	25.13	-251.30	100	2,513.00	10,000	24.47	102.70
	II	-9	25.82	-232.38	81	2,091.42	6,561	24.54	105.22
	III	-8	26.59	-212.72	64	1,701.76	4,096	24.63	107.96
	IV	-7	26.96	-188.72	49	1,321.04	2,401	24.75	108.93
1975	I	-6	26.73	-160.38	36	962.28	1,296	24.89	107.39
	II	-5	26.23	-104.92	25	655.75	625	25.06	104.67
	III	-4	25.99	-103.96	16	415.84	256	25.25	102.93
	IV	-3	26.07	-78.21	9	234.63	81	25.46	102.40
1976	I	-2	26.02	-52.04	4	104.08	16	25.70	101.25
	II	-1	26.27	-26.27	1	26.27	1	25.96	101.19
	III	0	26.40	0	0	0	0	26.25	100.57
	IV	1	26.39	26.39	1	26.39	1	26.56	99.36
1977	I	2	26.01	52.02	4	104.04	16	26.89	96.73
	II	3	26.41	79.23	9	237.69	81	27.25	96.92
	III	4	26.42	105.68	16	422.72	256	27.93	94.59
	IV	5	26.40	132.00	25	660.00	625	28.04	94.15
1978	I	6	26.89	161.34	36	968.04	1,296	28.47	94.45
	II	7	27.61	193.27	49	1,352.89	2,401	29.83	95.44
	III	8	28.29	226.32	64	1,810.56	4,096	29.41	96.19
	IV	9	28.82	259.38	81	2,334.42	6,561	29.92	96.32
1979	I	10	29.85	298.50	100	2,985.00	10,000	30.44	98.06
	II	11	30.84	339.24	121	3,731.64	14,641	31.00	99.48
	III	12	31.94	383.28	144	4,599.36	20,736	31.57	101.17
	IV	13	33.05	429.65	169	5,585.45	28,561	32.18	102.70
1980	I	14	35.29	494.06	196	6,916.84	38,416	32.80	107.59
	II		785.73	606.34	2,030	56,376.81	255,374		

Sums

$$b = \frac{\Sigma xY}{\Sigma x^2} = \frac{606.34}{2,030} = 0.2987$$

$\Sigma Y = na + c\Sigma x^2$

$\Sigma x^2 Y = a\Sigma x^2 + c\Sigma x^2$

$785.73 = 29a + 2,030c$

$56,376.81 = 2,030a + 255,374c$

$a = 26.2471$

$c = 0.0121$

$Y_t = 26.2471 + 0.2987x + 0.0121x^2$

$x = 0$ for 1976 III quarter

(j)   The trend values represent the quarterly sums of home mortgage rates for a given quarter had seasonal, cyclical, and irregular factors not been present.

106

(l)

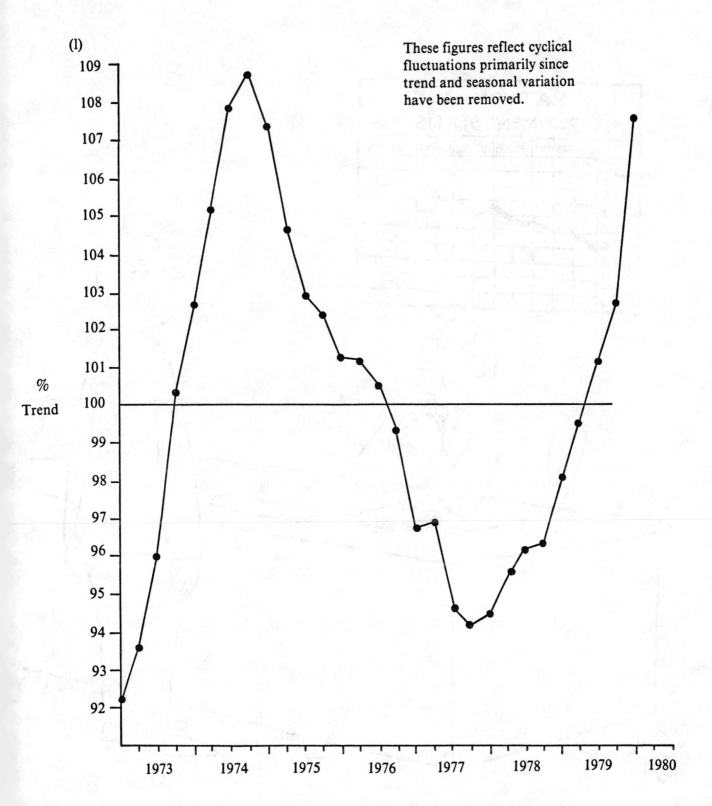

These figures reflect cyclical
fluctuations primarily since
trend and seasonal variation
have been removed.

"Yes, Farber—You wished to speak to me?"

Lesson 15-1 Time Relatives and Statistical Mischief

In the text, we noted that index numbers can produce erroneous impressions and may be used by unscrupulous people or organizations to mislead. The following excerpt from *How Numbers Lie* shows how time relatives, when based on numbers rather than on percentages, can produce misleading impressions when the population is either contracting or expanding in an orderly fashion (Runyon, 1981, pp. 93-97).

There are three things in life that are certain: death, taxes, and economic indexes. If anything can be measured over time—inflation, employment, unemployment, expenditures, wages and sin—you can be certain that an economist has devised an index to monitor its temporal fluctuations. One of the favorite devices is a *fixed-base time ratio* (also called time relative, percentage relative, and a host of other minor variations). In this type of index, you select a given year as the base year and express everything before and after it in relation to that year. Take a look at table 1. It shows the number of unemployed persons (in millions) between 1950 and 1979. To construct a time ratio with these data, select a year—any year—as your base year. For illustrative purposes, I arbitrarily selected 1970 as the base year. Now divide the number of unemployed found each year by 4.1 (the number of unemployed in 1970) and multiply by 100 in order to express the change as a percentage. You obtain the time ratio found in the last column of the table.

Time indexes are very useful tools. They provide a wealth of information at a glance. We know immediately that any year with an index below 100 means that the value for that year is less than the base. This is good news if we're talking about unemployment, crime statistics, automobile accidents, wholesale price index, or bubble gum sales. On the other hand, it's very bad if we're looking at gross national product, hourly wages, output per person-hour, or attendance at discos. Looking at table 1, we see that 1966 through 1969 were halcyon years with respect to unemployment. If you think back a moment, you'll recall that they also achieved some notoriety as years of social unrest, highlighted by protests against the Vietnam War.

But there is still something wrong with table 1. Note that the time ratio is based on the *number* of unemployed. Now, if the work force is changing from year to year, these data may be misleading. What if the total *number* of of wage earners is increasing each year (as it is) and the percentage of unemployed remains the same? In this event, the number of unemployed *must* go up. Failure to realize this fact may result in a bunch of misleading statements. A prime contender is any so-called crime statistic. Politicians wishing to embarass the

Table 1 Number of unemployed persons, in millions, and time ratio index based on a fixed year of 1970.

Year	Number Unemployed	Time Ratio	Year	Number Unemployed	Time Ratio
1960	3.9	95.1	1970	4.1	100.0
1961	4.7	114.6	1971	5.0	122.0
1962	3.9	95.1	1972	4.8	117.1
1963	4.1	100.0	1973	4.3	104.9
1964	3.8	92.7	1974	5.2	126.8
1965	3.4	82.9	1975	8.1	197.6
1966	2.9	70.7	1976	7.5	182.9
1967	3.0	73.2	1977	7.0	170.7
1968	2.8	68.3	1978	6.1	148.8
1969	2.8	68.3	1979*	6.1	148.8

*Estimated on the basis of data for the first nine months in 1979.

incumbent are not above such proclamations as "Crime, all sorts of crime, is up all over the state. We had more murders, homicides, rapes, burglaries, and drug abuse cases last year than during any preceding year in our history. The incumbent is clearly soft on crime."

The way out of this statistical mischief is to base the time ratio on proportional or percentage increases. For example, we could modify the entries in table 1 to represent the proportion of the total work force that is unemployed during any given year. Similarly, adult crime data could be expressed in terms of the proportion or percentage of adults in the population. When table 1 is redone to express these *rates* of unemployment, we obtain the following table (table 2).

Table 2 Time ratio of the proportion of unemployed in which the percentage for any given year is obtained by dividing the number of unemployed by the total work force for that year and multiplying by 100.

Year	Percentage Unemployed	Time Ratio	Year	Percentage Unemployed	Time Ratio
1960	5.6	114.3	1970	4.9	100.0
1961	6.7	136.7	1971	5.9	120.4
1962	5.5	112.2	1972	5.6	114.3
1963	5.7	116.3	1973	4.9	100.0
1964	5.2	106.1	1974	5.6	114.3
1965	4.5	91.8	1975	8.5	173.5
1966	3.8	77.6	1976	7.7	157.1
1967	3.8	77.6	1977	7.0	142.9
1968	3.6	73.5	1978	6.0	122.4
1969	3.5	71.4	1979	5.8	118.4

The difference that this change can make is dramatically demonstrated in figure 1. Note that the solid line representing the number of unemployed *underestimates* the *rate* of unemployment for all years before 1970, the base year. For example, looking at the solid line, we might judge 1961 to have been a sort of average year on the unemployment scene. It ranks ninth in number of unemployed over a twenty-year period. However, when we look at the dashed line, we see that as a matter of actual fact, the *rate* of unemployment for that year was the fourth highest over the same twenty-year period. Note that both of these are perfectly legitimate ways of showing data. Neither involves lying, deception, or chicanery in and of itself. But it's so easy to seduce the reader into drawing false conclusions, particularly if you are somewhat lax in labeling the figures and tables.

There's even more you can do, if you have mind to deceive. So far we have said nothing about choosing the base year. By an astute selection, you can convey almost any impression you desire. I hasten to note that I'm talking about *impressions*, not reality. The truth is that no matter what base year you choose, they all tell precisely the same statistical story. One can easily be transformed into another. But they *seem* to tell different tales, and that provides ample opportunity for deception.

Take a look at table 2 and figure 2. When the very lowest year is used as the base, all other years show higher rates of unemployment. Indeed, 1975-1977 looks like the Great Depression.

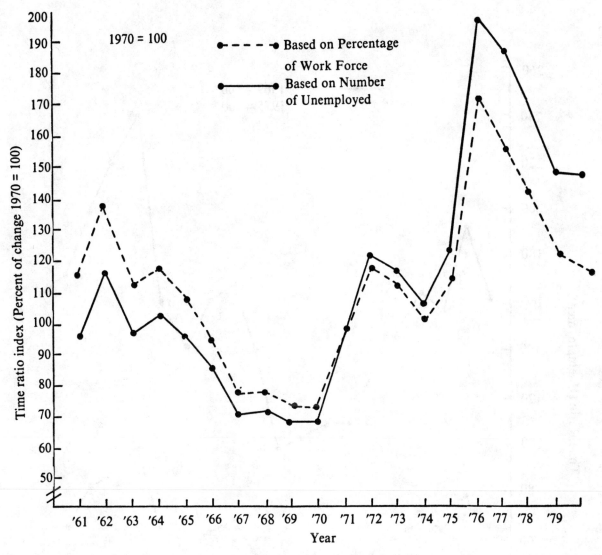

Fig. 1 Two Different Perspectives. Two time ratios based on the same unemployment data but differing in the impressions they convey. The solid line is based on the numbers of unemployed during each of the years. The dashed line is adjusted to reflect the percentage of the total work force that was unemployed during each year.

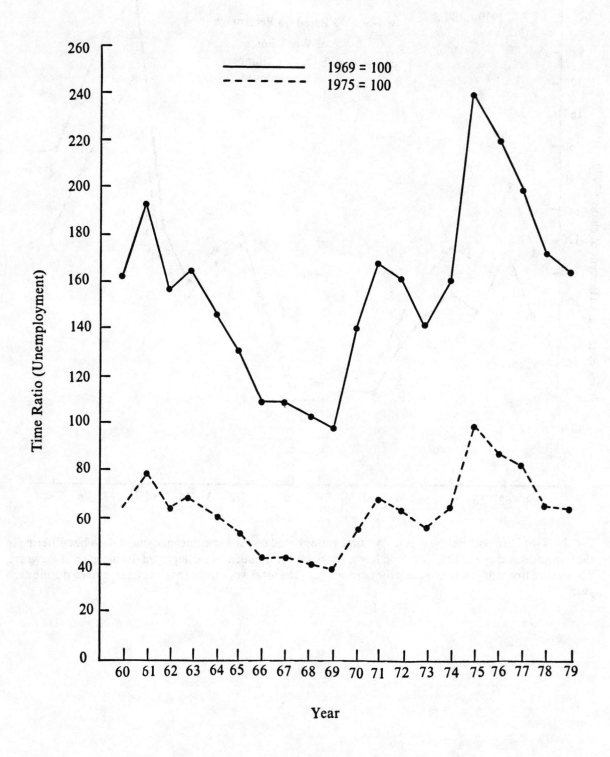

Fig. 2 The Same Information? Different impressions are conveyed by use of different base years when presenting graph of time ratios. When 1969 is used as base year, unemployment figures appear to be high. When 1975 is base year, unemployment figures appear to be low. In actuality, both graphs convey precisely the same statistical information.

Multiple-Choice Items

1. The following $I_p = \dfrac{P_n}{P_o} \times 100$ represents: a) an unweighted price relative; b) a weighted price relative; c) a quantity relative; d) a value relative.

2. The following $I_o = \dfrac{P_n Q_n}{P_o Q_o} \times 100$ represents: a) an unweighted price relative; b) a weighted price relative; c) a quantity relative; d) a value relative.

3. The difference between the percentage relative for value and the percentage relative for quantity represents: a) the percentage relative for price; b) inflationary factors; c) rounding errors; d) none of above.

4. When more than one variable makes up an index, it is referred to as a: a) multi-variable index; b) variable index; c) composite index; d) quantity index.

5. An unweighted aggregate price index: a) fails to weigh for differences in price; b) fails to weigh for differences in quantity; c) weighs for quantity but not for price; d) none of the above.

Items 6-10 are based on the following chart.

Item	Prices in 1975	Prices in 1981
Milk (pint)	19.6	25.0
Round steak	188.5	197.3
Flour (pound)	19.9	20.2
Eggs, A, large	77.0	98.0

6. Using 1975 as a base, the index for milk, expressed as a proportion, is: a) 0.78; b) 0.22; c) 0.28; d) 1.28.

7. The simple average of relative index is: a) 111.64; b) 0.90; c) 115.25; d) 461.00.

8. The prepare a Laspeyres index of these commodities, we would require: a) quantities for the base year; b) quantities for both the base year and the period of interest; c) quantities for the period of interest; c) none of the above.

9. To prepare a Paasche index, we would require: a) quantities for the base year; b) quantities for both the base year and the period of interest; c) quantities for the period of interest; d) none of the above.

10. In preparing a fixed weight aggregate index: a) any period may be used to obtain weights; b) we may focus on periods that are more representative of usual quantities; c) the weights need not all be based in one period; d) all of the above.

11. In weighted quantity indexes: a) quantities are used as weights; b) prices are used as weights; c) both quantities and prices are used as weights; d) none of the above.

12. The following formula

$$\frac{\Sigma\left(\dfrac{Q_n}{Q_o} \times 100\right)\left(Q_o P_o\right)}{\Sigma Q_o P_o}$$

represents: a) a Paasche index; b) a Lespeyres index; c) an unweighted average of relatives index; d) a weighted average of relatives index.

13. To shift the base of index numbers: a) we must continue to use the same series of index numbers, complete with original base; b) we divide each index number by the index number for the new base year and multiply by 100; c) we cannot accomplish this shift without major modifications in the data base; d) both a and b.

14. A change from 140 in June, 1981, to 142 in July, 1981, represents: a) an increase of 2 percent over one month; b) an increase of 1.43 percent; c) a decrease of 2 percent over the period; d) an increase of 1.41 percent.

Answers: 1 a; 2. d; 3. b; 4. c; 5. b; 6. d; 7. c; 8. a; 9. c; 10. d; 11. a; 12. d; 13. d; 14. b

Exercises

1. The table below shows the number of murders, by category, between 1965 and 1977 inclusive.

   (a) Prepare time relative indexes for each category, using 1970 as the base year.
   (b) Construct line drawings of the change in time relatives for each category, using 1970 as the base year.
   (c) How does the relative frequency of murder by guns compare in recent years with murders by the various other methods?

	Guns	Cutting or Stabbing	Blunt Objects	Strangu-lation	Drownings, Arson & Other
1965	5,015	2,021	505	894	338
66	5,660	2,134	516	896	346
67	6,998	2,200	589	957	370
68	8,105	2,317	713	936	432
69	8,876	2,534	613	1,038	513
70	9,039	2,424	604	1,031	551
71	10,712	3,017	645	1,295	514
72	10,379	2,974	672	1,291	516
73	11,249	2,985	848	1,445	596
74	12,474	3,228	976	1,417	537
75	12,061	3,245	1,001	1,646	689
76	10,592	2,956	806	1,330	921
77	11,274	3,440	849	1,431	1,039

Source: Information Please Almanac, 1980, Simon & Schuster, New York, NY.

2. It is possible to derive two types of percentages for the data in Exercise 1. If you sum across rows and then convert each category into a percentage figure, you will obtain the relative number of murders in each category for each year. If you sum the categories and divide each sum into the number of murders committed in each category each year, you will obtain an indication of annual changes in crime rate per category.

   (a) Find the category of murders committed in each category during each year.
   (b) Convert the percentages obtained in (a) into time relatives, using 1970 as the base year.
   (c) Note the index numbers in each category for each year. Does any category appear to show a greater rate of change relative to the other categories?

3. A retail furniture outlet compiled the following record of sales in four categories of furniture during the years 1975 and 1981.

	1975		1981	
	Price	Quantity	Price	Quantity
Book cases	689	120	1,060	150
Sofas	540	400	740	370
Beds	480	310	590	450
Dining Sets	1,040	90	1,220	110

(a) Find the unweighted aggregate price index, using 1975 as the base year.

(b) Find the unweighted aggregate quantity index, using 1975 as the base year.

(c) Find the simple weighted index, using 1975 as the base year.

(d) Find the Paasche index, using 1975 as the base year and 1981 as the given year.

(e) Find the Laspeyres index, using 1975 as the base year and 1981 as the given year.

Answers

1. a.

	Guns	Cutting or Stabbing	Blunt Objects	Strangu- lation	Drownings, Arson & Others
1965	55.5	83.4	83.6	86.7	61.3
1966	62.6	88.0	85.4	86.9	62.8
1967	77.4	90.8	97.5	92.8	67.2
1968	89.7	95.6	118.0	90.8	78.4
1969	98.2	104.5	101.5	107.7	93.1
1970	100.0	100.0	100.0	100.0	100.0
1971	118.5	124.5	106.8	125.6	93.3
1972	114.8	122.7	111.3	125.2	93.6
1973	124.4	123.1	140.4	140.2	108.2
1974	138.0	133.2	161.6	137.4	97.5
1975	133.4	133.9	165.7	159.7	125.0
1976	117.2	121.9	133.4	129.0	167.2
1977	124.7	141.9	140.6	138.8	188.6

b.

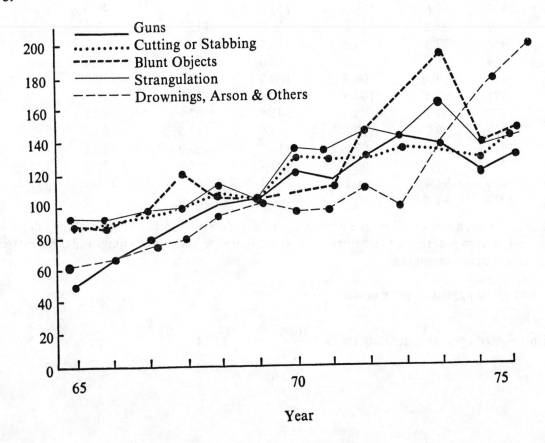

115

(c) Although the gun is by far the murder weapon of choice, the relative increase in the number of murders by gun has been generally less than the relative increase in other ways of committing murder.

2. a.

	Guns	Cutting or Stabbing	Blunt Objects	Strangulation	Drownings, Arson & Others
			Percent		
1965	57.2	23.0	5.8	10.2	3.9
1966	59.3	22.3	5.4	9.4	3.6
1967	63.0	19.8	5.3	8.6	3.3
1968	64.8	18.5	5.7	7.5	3.4
1969	65.4	18.7	4.4	4.5	3.8
1970	66.2	17.8	4.4	7.6	4.0
1971	66.2	18.6	4.0	8.0	3.2
1972	65.6	18.8	4.2	8.2	3.3
1973	65.7	17.4	5.0	8.4	3.5
1974	66.9	17.3	5.2	7.6	2.9
1975	64.7	17.4	5.4	8.8	3.7
1976	63.8	17.8	4.9	8.0	5.5
1977	62.5	19.1	4.7	7.9	5.8

b.

	Guns	Cutting or Stabbing	Blunt Objects	Strangulation	Drownings, Arson & Others
1965	86.4	129.2	131.8	134.2	97.5
1966	89.6	125.3	122.7	123.7	90.0
1967	95.2	111.2	120.5	113.2	82.5
1968	97.9	103.9	129.5	98.7	85.0
1969	98.8	105.1	100.0	59.2	95.0
1970	100.0	100.0	100.0	100.0	100.0
1971	100.0	104.5	90.9	105.3	80.0
1972	99.1	105.6	95.5	107.9	82.5
1973	99.2	97.8	113.6	110.5	87.5
1974	101.1	97.2	118.2	100.0	72.5
1975	97.7	97.8	122.7	115.8	92.5
1976	96.4	100.0	111.4	105.3	137.5
1977	94.4	107.3	106.8	103.9	145.0

(c) The index numbers based on the percentage of murders committed by guns show relatively little variation from year to year. In contrast, those attributed to arson, drowning, and other causes show much greater fluctuations.

Unweighted aggregate price index = $\frac{3610}{2749}$ x 100 = 131.3.

b. Unweighted aggregate quantity index = $\frac{1080}{920}$ x 100 = 117.4.

116

c. Simple weighted index = $\dfrac{832500}{541080}$ x 100 = 153.9.

d. Paasche index = $\dfrac{832500}{633550}$ x 100 = 131.4

e. Laspeyres index = $\dfrac{715900}{541080}$ x 100 = 132.3

"Cheap money or no cheap money, it's still something to be a billionnaire."

3-1. (b)

X	$(X-3)^2$	$(X-4)^2$	$(X-\bar{X})^2$	$(X-6)^2$	$(X-7)^2$
3	0	1	4	9	16
4	1	0	1	4	9
5	4	1	0	1	4
6	9	4	1	0	1
7	16	9	4	1	0
Total	30	15	10	15	30

3-3. $\Sigma fX = 982$

$n = 60$

$\bar{X} = 16.37$

As expected, there is a slight disparity between the mean obtained from the individual measurements (16.23) and the mean obtained from the grouped data (16.37).

3-5. In this case, the weight of the shares-to-be purchased is the unknown. Let y equal the unknown weight. Algebraically, we know

$$\bar{X}_w = \frac{\Sigma wX}{\Sigma w}.$$

With the purchase of the additional shares (y), the equation reads:

$$3.50 = \frac{\Sigma wX + 2.50y}{\Sigma w + y}$$

$$3.50\Sigma w + 3.50y = \Sigma wX + 2.50y$$

$$(3.50)(15,000) + 3.50y = 65,575 + 2.50y$$
$$y = 65,575 - 52,500$$
$$= 13,075$$

With the new purchase, the portfolio will appear as follows:

(X) Price per Share	*(w)* Number of Shares	wX
2.50	13,075	32687.5
3.00	5,300	15900.0
4.75	4,500	21375.0
5.00	2,600	13000.0
5.50	1,600	8800.0
6.50	1,000	6500.0
Total	28,075	98262.5

$$\bar{X}_w = \frac{98262.5}{28075} = 3.50$$

3-15.

	Food	Housing	Apparel	Transp.	Medical	Enter	Other
ΣX	58.3	51.6	29.3	46.9	55.9	37.1	41.6
ΣX^2	591.75	431.26	138.61	398.33	508.91	226.73	262.34
$\overline{X}$	8.329	7.371	4.186	6.700	7.986	5.300	5.943
s	4.207	2.912	1.631	3.744	3.228	2.240	1.587

Food shows greatest variability

3-17. A standard deviation of 0 means *no* variability; therefore, the price was $13.50 *every* day of the month.

Chapter 4

4-13. (A) = increase granted in 1980
(B) = increase granted in 1979
(C) = increase granted in 1978

$p(A \text{ and } B) = p(B)p(A|B) = (0.60)(0.30) = 0.18$
$p(A \text{ and } C) = p(C)p(A|C) = (0.43)(0.50) = 0.215$

Thus, a company granted an increase in 1978 has a slightly better chance of approval in 1980.

4-17.

	Hired A_1	Not Hired A_2	Marginal
Male B_1	0.20	0.50	0.70
Female B_2	0.20	0.10	0.30
Marginal	0.40	0.60	

(a) $p(A_1|B_1) = \dfrac{0.20}{0.70} = 0.29$

(b) $p(A_1|B_2) = \dfrac{0.20}{0.30} = 0.67$

4-23. (a) No, since p(A and B) would equal zero if they were mutually exclusive.
(b) No, since p(A and B) would equal p(A)p(B) if they were independent.

4-25. (a) No, since p(A and B) would equal zero if they were mutually exclusive.
(b) Yes, since p(A and B) = p(A)p(B) = (0.35)(0.66) = 0.231.

4-27. Let (A) = sale is made; p(A) = 0.80;

Let (B) = offer made in the first month; p(B) = 0.50;

p(A and B) = 0.40

$p(A|B) = \dfrac{p(A \text{ and } B)}{p(B)} = \dfrac{0.40}{0.50} = 0.80$

Since p(A|B) = p(A), the two events are independent. That is, the probability that Lila will sell the property [p(A)] is not dependent upon an offer being made the first month.

4-29. (c) Since the workers are selected at random, each sample point has an equal probability. There are 10 sample points, each with a probability of $1/10 = 0.10$. Thus, p(A) = 4/10 = 0.40.

(e) $p(A \text{ and } B) = \dfrac{1}{10} = 0.10$ since there is only one sample point corresponding to this event [i.e.,(1,5)].

(f) No (A) and (B) are not independent:

$$p(A|B) = \frac{p(A \text{ and } B)}{p(B)} = \frac{0.10}{0.40} = 0.25$$

$$p(A|B) = 0.25 \neq p(A) = 0.40.$$

(g) No (A) and (B) are not mutually exclusive since $p(A \text{ and } B) \neq 0$.

(h) $p(A \text{ or } B) = p(A) + p(B) - p(A \text{ and } B)$
$\qquad\qquad = 0.40 + 0.40 - 0.10 = 0.70$

4-31. (A_1) = "Good" tenants (i.e., do not "skip out"); $p(A_1)$ = 94%

(A_2) = "bad" tenants (i.e., "skip out") $p(A_2)$ = 6%

(B_1) = good credit score; $p(B_1)$ = 85%

(B_2) = bad credit score; $p(B_2)$ = 15%

$p(A_1 \text{ and } B_1)$ = 80%

$$p(A_1|B_1) = \frac{p(A_1 \text{ and } B_1)}{p(B_1)} = \frac{80}{85} \times 100 = 94.12\%$$

4-33. (a) p(all 3 cannot) = (0.85)(0.85)(0.85) = 0.6141

(b) p(2 cannot and 1 can) = (0.85)(0.85)(0.15) + (0.85)(0.15)(0.85) + (0.15)(0.85)(0.85)
$\qquad\qquad\qquad\qquad = 0.1084$

p(at least 2 cannot) = p(2 cannot and 1 can) + p(all 3 cannot)
$\qquad\qquad\qquad = 0.1084 + 0.6141$
$\qquad\qquad\qquad = 0.7225$

(c) p(all 3 can) = (0.15)(0.15)(0.15)= 0.0034

4-35. Let (A) = acceptance at university.
$\qquad$(B) = from private school in Mass.

(a) $\quad p(A) = \dfrac{2,000}{11,180} = 0.1789$ or 17.89%

(b) $\quad p(B|A) = \dfrac{40}{2,000} = 0.02$ or 2%

(c) $p(A \text{ and } B) = p(A)p(B|A) = (0.1789)(0.02) = 0.0036$

4-37. (a) Mutually exclusive: No. p(A and B and C) $\neq$ 0. That is, all three conditions can occur simultaneously.

(b) Exhaustive: Yes. The way Gosden has set up the probabilities: p(A) + p(B) + p(C) = 1.00.

(c) Complementary: No because they are not mutually exclusive.

(d) Independent: No. The chances are that who and what you are, etc., will be related to whether or not you hit the right audience, have the right visuals, and vice versa.

4-39. (A_1) = no competition, $p(A_1)$ = 0.50

(A_2) = competition, $p(A_2)$ = 0.60

(B_1) = success

(B_2) = fail

Given no competition, the probability of success $p(B_1|A_1)$ = 0.80
Given competition, the probability of success: $p(B_1|A_1)$ = 0.60

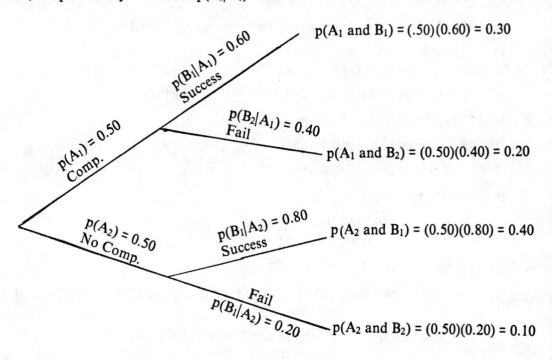

$p(success) = p(B_1) = p(A_1 \text{ and } B_1) + p(A_2 \text{ and } B_1) = 0.30 + 0.40 = 0.70.$

4.41. (A) = getting the disease; $p(A) = \dfrac{3}{100,000} = 0.00003$

(B) = used Rely
   $p(B|A)$ = given that the individual got the disease, the probability tht she used Rely = 0.70.

Therefore, $p(A \text{ and } B) = p(A)p(B|A)$
$$= (0.00003)(0.70)$$
$$= 0.000021$$

Chapter 5

5-1. (a) Using the addition rule for mutually exclusive events, p(0 or -1,000 or -2,000) = 0.1875 + 0.1250 + 0.0625 = 0.3750.

(b) p(3,000 or 4,000) = 0.1250 + 0.625 = 0.1875

(c) p(-1,000 or -2,000) = 0.1250 + 0.0625 = 0.1875

5-3. The net return on the bid can assume one of two different values. If she loses the bid, her return will be -$15,000 (p = 0.70); if she succeeds her gain will be $125,000 - $15,000 = $110,000 (p = 0.30).

X	p(X)	Xp(X)
-15,000	0.7	-10,500
+110,000	0.3	+33,000
		E(X) = 22,500

She should not bid since the expected net gain is less than the profit that would satisfy her employers.

5-5.

X	p(X)	Xp(X)
-5,000,000	0.85	-4,250,000
+195,000,000	0.15	+27,750,000

$$E(X) = + 23,500,000$$

Since the expected return is positive, it will explore the possibility in greater depth.

5-9. $P = 0.83, Q = 0.17, n = 4$

(a) $p(x=4)$ $= \dfrac{4!}{4!0!} (0.83)^4(0.17)^0$

            $= 0.4746$

(b) $p(\text{at least } 2) = p(x=2) + p(x=3) + p(x=4)$

     $p(x=2)$ $= \dfrac{4!}{2!2!} (0.83)^2(0.17)^2 = 6(0.6889)(0.0289)$

            $= 0.1195$

     $p(x=3)$ $= \dfrac{4!}{3!1!} (0.83)^3(0.17)^1$

            $= 0.3888$

     $p(x=4)$ $= 0.4746$

$p(\text{at least } 2) = 0.1195 + 0.3888 + 0.4746 = 0.9829$

5-13. $P = $ more than 2,000 square feet $= 0.15$
Q = less than 2,000 square feet $= 0.85$
$n = 15$

(a) $p[(n-x) \geqslant 10] = p(x \leqslant 5) = 0.0874 + 0.1156 + 0.2184 + 0.2856 + 0.2312 + 0.0449 = 0.9831$
(b) $p[n-x) \geqslant 6] = p(x \leqslant 9) = 0.9999$

5-15. $\lambda = \dfrac{36}{24} = 1.5$ $\mu = (1.5)(1) = 1.5$

Using Table IV, we find

            $p(x \geqslant 4) = 1 \quad p(x < 4)$

               $p(x=0) = 0.2231$
               $p(x=1) = 0.3347$
               $p(x=2) = 0.2510$
               $p(x=3) = 0.1255$

          $p(x \geqslant 4) = 1 - 0.9343 = 0.0657$

5-17. $\mu = nP = (120)(0.03) = 3.6$

     $p(x \geqslant 6) = 1 - p(x < 6) = 1 - 0.8442 = 0.1558$

This means that, even if *not* as effective as hoped, the probability is 0.16 that the circular will bring in 6 or more responses.

5-19. (a) $\quad z = \dfrac{0.78 - 0.75}{0.02} = 0.67 \qquad p = 0.2514$, using Column C.

(b) $\quad z = \dfrac{0.72 - 0.75}{0.02} = -0.67 \qquad p = 0.2514$, using Column C.

(c) If we define event A as too wide and event B as too narrow, $p(A \text{ or } B) = p(A) + p(B) = 0.5028$.

(d) If we define event C as a defective bolt, $p(C) = 0.5028$. The probability of selecting a defective bolt on two consecutive independent trials is $p(C \text{ and } C) = p(C)p(C) = (0.5028)^2 = 0.2528$.

(e) We may obtain this value by subtraction: $1 - 0.5028 = 0.4972$ or

$$z = 0.67, \ p = 0.2486, \text{ using Column B}$$
$$z = -0.67, \ p = \underline{0.2486}, \text{ using Column B}$$
$$0.4972$$

(f) If we define event D as a non-defective bolt, $p(D) = 0.4972$. Thus, $p(D \text{ and } D) = p(D)p(D) = (0.4972)^2 = 0.2472$.

5-21. $P = 0.40, Q = 0.60, n = 200$

$\mu = nP = 80; \qquad \sigma = \sqrt{nPQ} = 6.93$

$$z = \dfrac{70-80}{6.93} = -1.44, \ p = 0.0749$$

The probability is approximately 7 percent that fewer than 70 out of 200 people are fearful of violent crimes.

5-23. $P = 0.05$ (homes unlocked), $Q = 0.95, n = 200$

$\mu = (200)(0.05) = 10, \sigma = \sqrt{(200)(0.05)(0.95)} = \sqrt{9.5} = 3.08$

$$z = \dfrac{10 - 10}{3.08} = 0$$

Thus, the probability is 50 percent that 10 or more homes will be unlocked.

5-25.

X		p(X)	Xp(X)
22 days	(-220)+(-75) - 295	0.05	-14.75
30 days	(-300)+(-75) - 375	0.65	-243.75
60 days	(-600)+(-200) - 800	0.30	-240.00
			498.50

The landlord should collect approximately $500.00 security deposit.

5-27. (a) $\quad z = \dfrac{630 - 583}{50} = 0.94, \ p = 0.1736$

(B) $\quad z = \dfrac{430 - 583}{50} = -3.06, \ p = 0.0011$

(c) A probability of 90 percent that a battery will operate is the same as a probability of 10 percent that it will not. Thus, we find the z-score corresponding to 0.10 of the area beyond (Column C).

$X = 583 + (-1.28)(50)$
$ = 519$

124

5-29. (a) P = not resolved before trial = 0.05
Q = resolved before trial = 0.95
n = 10

(i) p[n-x) = 10] = p(x=0) = 0.5987
(ii) p[n-x)$\geqslant$6] = p(x$\leqslant$4) for P = 0.05, n = 10, = 0.9999

According to this result, it is almost certain that at least 6 of the cases will be resolved before trial.

(b) P = no money settlement to plaintiff = 0.055
Q = money settlement to plaintiff = 0.945
n = 10
p[(n-x)$\geqslant$4] = p(x$\leqslant$6)

To use the table, we shall have to round P to 0.05.
Thus, p(x$\leqslant$6) = 1.0000.
It is certainly worthwhile for the attorney to accept these cases on a contingency basis.

(c) p(A) = probability case resolved before trial = 0.95

p($\overline{A}$) = probability it was *not* resolved before trial = 0.05

p(B) = probability of money settlement to plaintiff = 0.945

p($\overline{B}$) = probability of *no* money settlement to plaintiff = 0.055

In order to answer this question, it is best to summarize all the information in a joint probability table:

	No Trial (A)	Trial ($\overline{A}$)	
Money to plaintiff (B)	0.9405	0.0045	0.9450
No money to plaintiff ($\overline{B}$)	0.0095	0.0455	0.0550
	0.9500	0.0500	

$$p(B|\overline{A}) = \frac{p(\overline{A} \text{ and } B)}{p(\overline{A})} = \frac{0.0045}{0.0455}$$

$$= 0.0989$$

Thus, the probability is slightly less than 10 percent that a plaintiff will win a money settlement given that the case has gone to trial. The probability that at least 5 will win money judgements = p(x$\geqslant$5) for P = 0.10 and n = 10 = 0.0016.

Therefore, if all the cases go to trial, the probability is very low (0.16%) that enough plaintiffs will win money damages to make it worthwhile for the attorney.

5-31. $z = \dfrac{2-4}{1} = -2.00$, p = 0.0228.

The chances are about 2 percent that your set will be serviced in time to see the program. Since the probability is so low, you should probably make alternative arrangements.

5-33. P = 0.0006, n = 1000
μ = (1000)(0.0006) = 0.6

(a) p(x=0) = 0.5488 (Approximately 50-50 chance none will be raped.)
(b) p(x$\geqslant$4) = 0.0034 (Probability is less than 1 percent that 4 or more will be raped.)

5-35. $\mu = (900)\left(\dfrac{1}{60}\right) = 15.0;$

$p(x>10) = 0.8815.$

Thus, do the most carefully laid plans of mice and men oft go awry.

5-37. In order to answer this question, we must calculate the expected value for each alternative.

(1) Regular passbook account at 5.5 percent:

	Interest (X)	p(X)	Xp(X)
1 mo.	45.83	0.05	+2.29
2 mo.	91.66	0.05	+4.58
3 mo.	137.49	0.05	+6.87
4 mo.	183.32	0.15	+27.50
5 mo.	229.15	0.20	+45.83
6 mo.	274.98	0.50	+137.49
			E(X) = +224.56

(2) 6 month money market certificate. At 10.5 percent she will accrue interest of $87.50 a month. However, if she withdraws before 6 months, she will lose 90 days interest or $262.50.

	Interest (X)	p(X)	Xp(X)
1 mo.	-175.00	0.05	-8.75
2 mo.	-87.50	0.05	-4.375
3 mo.	0	0.05	0
4 mo.	+87.50	0.15	+13.125
5 mo.	+175.00	0.20	+35.00
6 mo.	+525.00	0.50	+262.50
			E(X) = +297.50

She should choose the money-market certificate since the expected return is greater.

5-41. P = 0.50, Q = 0.50, n = 500, x = 400

$\mu = nP = 250 \qquad \sigma = \sqrt{(500)(0.5)(0.5)} = \sqrt{125} = 11.18$

$z = \dfrac{400 - 250}{11.18} = 13.42$

Since the obtained z is so large, it does not even appear on the table. Thus, we can safely say that the probability is extremely low. If the consumer advocates' estimate is correct, it is very unlikely that the survey will support the industry's position.

5-43. P = defective = 0.01
Q = non-defective = 0.99
n = 10, x = 2

Using Table I to find the probability of exactly 2 out of 10 when P = 0.01:

$$p(x=2) = 0.0042$$

Thus, the probability of finding exactly two defectives out of 10 when P = 0.01 is a highly unlikely event.

5-45. $\mu = nP = (60)(0.50); \sigma = \sqrt{nPQ} = \sqrt{(60)(0.5)(0.5)} = \sqrt{15} = 3.87$

$\qquad = 30$

$z = \dfrac{60 - 30}{3.87} = 7.75.$

This result is so rare that there is no tabled value. We can be sure that $p < 0.0001$. If you own a calculator with the key y^x, you may obtain the exact probability. Enter 0.5, depress y^x, and then enter 60. This shows P raised to the sixtieth power.

Thus, $p(x = 60, n = 60) = P^{60} = (1/2)^{60} = 86736174^{-19}$. The probability is so infinitesimally small (about 9 in a trillion), it is unlikely that the event occurred by chance.

5-47. (a)

	X	p(X)	Xp(X)
Ladder	1.50	0.20	-0.30
Laundry carts	+3.50	0.80	+2.80
			+2.50

He would make $2.50 on every order.

(b)

	X	p(X)	Xp(X)
Ladder	-1.50	0.80	-1.20
Laundry cart	+3.50	0.20	+.70
			-.50

He lost 50¢ on every order.

5-49. (a) $z = \dfrac{40 - 44.41}{2.50} = -1.76, p = 0.0392$

(b) $z = \dfrac{50 - 44.41}{2.50} = 2.24, p = 0.4875$

$p(40 \leqslant X \leqslant 50) = 0.0392 + 0.4875 = 0.5267$

(c) $z = \dfrac{35 - 44.41}{2.50} = -3.76, p = 0.4999$

$p(35 \leqslant X \leqslant 40) = 0.4999 - 0.0392 = 0.4607$

(d) $z = -1.76, p = 0.0392 + 0.5000 = 0.5392$

Chapter 6

6-9. $s_{\bar{X}} = \dfrac{s}{\sqrt{n}} = \dfrac{7.15}{\sqrt{112}} = 0.68$

(a) $z = \dfrac{\pm 2.00}{0.68} = \pm 2.94; p = 0.9968$

(b) $z = \dfrac{\pm 1.50}{0.68} = \pm 2.21; p = 0.9728$

(c) $z = \dfrac{\pm 1.00}{0.68} = \pm 1.47; p = 0.8584$

(d) $z = \dfrac{\pm 0.50}{0.68} = \pm 0.74; p = 0.5408$

6.11   (a) $\sigma \overline{x} = \dfrac{500}{5} = 100; \quad z = \dfrac{\pm 100}{100} = \pm 1.00, p = 0.3174$

(b) $z = \dfrac{2000-1700}{100}\ 3.00, p = 0.0013$

(c) $z = \dfrac{2000-2500}{100} = -5.00.$

Since z = -5.00 is so high, it does not even appear on the table, we can safely place the probability close to 1.00.

6-13. In this exercise, we were not told the form of the distribution in the population. However, since n>30, according to the Central-limit theorem, we can reasonably assume that the sampling distribution of the mean is essentially normal. Thus, we shall use this as our model in determining probabilities.

(a) $\sigma \overline{x} = \dfrac{\sigma}{\sqrt{n}} = \dfrac{1.5}{\sqrt{36}} = 0.25$

$z = \dfrac{-0.75}{0.25} = -3.00 \qquad z = \dfrac{+0.75}{0.25} = 3.00$

The probability that the estimated mean will lie within ± 0.75 ppb of the true mean is 0.9974, or approximately 100 percent.

(b) $\sigma \overline{x} = \dfrac{2.9}{6} = 0.48$

$z = \dfrac{-0.75}{0.48} = -1.56 \qquad z = \dfrac{0.75}{0.48} = 1.56$

The probability that the estimated mean will lie within ± 0.75 ppb of the population mean is 0.8806, or approximately 88 percent.

The increased variability (1.5 vs 2.9) in the population results in greater variability in the sampling distribution of the mean. The greater the variability ($\sigma \overline{x}$ = 0.48 vs $\sigma \overline{x}$ = 0.25), the less the chances are that the obtained $\overline{X}$ is closer to the population mean. In other words, greater variability reduces reliability.

6.17.   (a) $\sigma \overline{x} = \left(\dfrac{1000}{\sqrt{5}}\right)\left(\sqrt{\dfrac{50-5}{49}}\right) = (446.43)(0.9183) = 409.96$

$z = \dfrac{\pm 500}{409.96} = \pm 1.22; p = 0.7776$

(b) $\sigma \overline{x} = \left(\dfrac{1000}{\sqrt{10}}\right)\left(\sqrt{\dfrac{40}{49}}\right) = (316.46)(0.9035) = 285.92$

$z = \dfrac{\pm 500}{285.92} = \pm 1.75; p = 0.9198$

(c) $\quad \sigma\bar{x} = \left(\dfrac{1000}{\sqrt{25}}\right)\left(\sqrt{\dfrac{25}{29}}\right) = (200)(0.7143) = 142.86$

$$z = \dfrac{\pm 500}{142.86} = \pm 3.50;\ p = 0.9996$$

6.19. (a) $\quad N = 100,\ n = 10$

$\sigma\bar{x} = (316.46)(0.9535) = 301.74$

$$z = \dfrac{\pm 500}{301.74} = \pm 1.66;\ p = 0.9030$$

(b) $\quad N = 500,\ n = 10$

$\sigma\bar{x} = (316.46)(0.9909) = 313.58$

$$z = \dfrac{\pm 500}{313.58} = \pm 1.59;\ p = 0.8882$$

6-21. (a) $\quad \sigma\bar{x} = \dfrac{\sigma}{\sqrt{n}} = \dfrac{0.75}{\sqrt{20}} = 0.17$

$$z = \dfrac{\pm 0.5}{0.17} = \pm 2.94,\ p = 0.0032$$

(b) $\quad \sigma\bar{x} = \dfrac{1.50}{\sqrt{20}} = 0.34$

$$z = \dfrac{\pm 0.5}{0.34} = \pm 1.47,\ p = 0.1416$$

The probability that the sample means will differ from the assumed population means by more than a half-minute is greater for lunch-time because the population variability is greater.

6-31. (a) $\quad n = 10;\ \sigma\bar{x} = 4.75$

make money: $z(X \geqslant 75) = \dfrac{75\text{-}82}{4.75} = -1.47 \quad p = 0.9292$

lose money: $z(X \leqslant 60) = -3.79;\ p = 0.0001$

(b) $\quad n = 25;\ \sigma\bar{x} = 3.00$

make money: $z = -2.33;\ p = 0.9901$
lose money: $z = -4.00;\ p = 0.00003$

6-33. (a) A simple random sample might be obtained by using a table of random digits. Each member of the two populations would be separately numbered. The samples would then be selected by choosing the member whose number corresponds to the random digit in the table.

(b) A systematic random sample could be obtained by first randomly selecting one member from each population as the "starting point". Then, for example, every 50th or 100th member would be selected (depending on the size of each sample) from each population.

(c) To obtain a stratified random sample, we first need to divide our populations into subgroups. In this example, we might define our strata in terms of the fields in which they work. We would then obtain random samples from within each population stratum.

(d) We might obtain a cluster sample by dividing the populations into different geographical areas. We would then randomly select certain geographical areas and sample all members of each population in those areas.

Chapter 7

7-9. (a) 17.5% increase from 18 days = 21.15 days
3.0% standard deviation = 0.54 days

Since $\dfrac{n}{N}$ = 0.13, we use the finite correction factor to find the corrected standard error of the mean:

$$s_{\overline{X}} = \frac{0.54}{\sqrt{400}} \sqrt{\frac{3000-400}{2999}}$$

$$= (0.027)(0.9311)$$
$$= 0.025$$

95 percent confidence limits: $21.15 \pm (0.96)(0.025)$ = 21.101 to 21.199

(b) 95 percent confidence limits for total: (21.101)(3000) to (21.199)(3000); 63,303 to 63,597

7-11. (a) $\overline{X}_1 = 66.50$ $\overline{X}_2 = 55.86$

$s_1^2 = 32.27$ $s_2^2 = 32.13$

$\overline{X}_1 - \overline{X}_2 = 10.64$

(b) $s_{\overline{X}_1-\overline{X}_2} = \sqrt{\dfrac{32.27}{14} + \dfrac{32.13}{14}}$

$$= 2.14, \text{ df} = 26$$

95 percent confidence interval = $10.64 \pm (2.056)(2.14)$ = 6.24 to 15.04

Thus, at the 95 percent confidence level, we feel that the view of the "patrol cars" reduced the mean speed of cars between 6.25 and 15.04 miles per hour.

7-13. (a) $s_{\overline{p}} = \sqrt{\dfrac{(0.06)(0.94)}{1000}} = 0.0075$

90 percent confidence interval = $0.06 \pm (1.645)(0.0075)$
$$= 0.0476 \text{ to } 0.0723$$

7.15 (a) $n = \left(\dfrac{1.96}{0.02}\right)^2 (0.47)(0.53)$

$$= 2392$$

7-19. Point estimate of $\mu_1 - \mu_2$ is $\overline{X}_1 - \overline{X}_2$ = 12.8 - 11.5 = 1.3

$$s_{\overline{X}_1-\overline{X}_2} = \sqrt{\frac{3^2 + 2.5^2}{50}} = 0.55$$

The probability that the error of estimation is less than (1.96)(0.55) or 1.08 minutes is 95 percent. Since the point estimate is 1.3, there is a high probability that there is a true difference in mean time per call.

7-21. Point estimate for $(\mu_1-\mu_2)$ is $\overline{X}_1 - \overline{X}_2$ = 12.5 - 8.5 = 4.0 days

$$s_{\overline{X}_1-\overline{X}_2} = \sqrt{\frac{(2.5)^2 + (3.5)^2}{9}}$$

$$= 1.43$$

95 percent confidence limits: df = 16, t = 2.12
$400 \pm (2.12)(1.43)$
0.97 to 7.03 days

7-23. $n = \left[\dfrac{(1.96)(1.9)}{0.25}\right]^2$

  = 221.9 or 222

7-27. (a) $\bar{p} = 0.02 \qquad s_{\bar{p}} = 0.00187$

  95 percent confidence interval = $0.02 \pm (0.96)(0.001887) = 0.0163$ to 0.0237

  (b) 95 percent confidence interval of total number = 12225 to 17775

7-29. $s_{\bar{x}} = (2)\sqrt{\dfrac{200\text{-}25}{199}} = 1.88$

  95 percent confidence limits = 431.12 to 438.88

  Now that we are given the number in the population (N = 200), we see that $\dfrac{n}{N} = 0.125$; thus, we must correct $s_{\bar{x}}$ by the finite correction factor.

7-31. (a) $\bar{p} = 0.1511 \qquad \bar{q} = 0.8489 \qquad s_{\bar{p}} = 0.0169$

  90 percent confidence interval = $0.1511 \pm (1.645)(0.0169) = 0.1233$ to 0.1789

  (b) 90 percent estimate of total sales potential = 3,699,000 to 5,367,000 point estimate of total = 4,533,000

7-33. $\bar{p} = \dfrac{19}{70} = 0.271 \quad s_{\bar{p}} = \left(\sqrt{\dfrac{(0.271)(0.729)}{70}}\right) \cdot \left(\sqrt{\dfrac{250\text{-}70}{249}}\right) = 0.038$

  (a) 95 percent confidence limits = $0.271 \pm (1.96)(0.038) = 0.197$ to 0.345
  (b) 95 percent confidence limits for total = $(250)(0.197)$ to $(250)(0.345)$
  $$= 49.25 \text{ to } 86.25$$

Chapter 8

8-7. 1. *Null hypothesis* (H_o): The mean ratio for California is equal to the mean ratio for the rest of the nation, i.e., $\mu = \mu_o = 11.20$.

  2. *Alternative hypothesis* (H_1): The mean ratio for California is different from the rest of the nation, i.e., $\mu \neq u_o \neq 11.20$. We use a non-directional H_1 since we are merely interested in whether California is different, not in the direction of the difference.

  3. *Statistical test:* We use the Student t-ratio since n < 30.

  4. *Significance level:* $\alpha = 0.05$.

  5. *Sampling distribution:* The sampling distribution is the t-distribution with df = 4.

  6. *Critical region:* $t \geqslant |2.776|$. Since H_1 is non-directional, the critical region consists of all values of $t \geqslant 2.776$ and $t \leqslant -2.776$.

  $\bar{X} = 2.94$, s = 3.18, $s_{\bar{x}} = 1.42$

  $$t = \dfrac{2.94 - 11.20}{1.42} = -5.817$$

Decision: We reject H_o since our obtained z falls in the critical region (i.e., $-5.817 < -2.776$). Thus, it appears that California is different from the rest of the country with respect to the ratio of swimming pool to spa/hot tub sales.

8-9. 1. *Null hypothesis* (H_o): The mean of the population requiring no helmet is less than or equal to the mean of the population requiring helmets, i.e., $\mu_1 \leqslant \mu_2$ or $\mu_1 - \mu_2 \leqslant 0$.

2. *Alternative hypothesis* (H_o): The mean of the population requiring no helmets is greater than the mean of the population requiring helmets, i.e., $\mu_1 > \sigma_2$, or $\mu_1 - \mu_2 > 0$. We choose a directional H_1 because we are specifically interested in whether repeal of the helmet law has led to an *increase* in fatalities.

3. *Statistical test:* We use the t-ratio because we are dealing with two small samples.

4. *Significance level:* $\alpha = 0.05$.

5. *Sampling distribution:* The sampling distribution is the t-distribution with df = 4 + 4 - 2 = 6.

6. *Critical region:* Since we have a directional H_1, the critical region consists of all values of $t \geqslant 1.943$.

$$s\overline{X}_1\text{-}\overline{X}_2 = 0.0203$$

$$t = \frac{0.2221 - 0.1036}{0.0203} = 5.837$$

Decision: Since our obtained t falls in the critical region, we reject H_o. States that do not require helmets have a significantly greater fatality rate than those that continue to require helmets.

8-11. H_o: $P = P_o = 0.25$

H_1: $P \neq P_o \neq 0.25$

Since hypotheses are formulated prior to data collection, we really have no basis for predicting direction.

$$z = \frac{0.52 - 0.25}{0.0155} = 17.42; \text{ Reject } H_o.$$

8-13. (a) H_o: $\mu \leqslant \mu_o \leqslant 6$

H_1: $\mu > \mu_o > 6$

We may use a directional H_1 since Harriet is interested in determining whether the new system *increases* waiting time.

$$z = \frac{7.2 - 6}{0.21} = 5.71$$

Reject H_o. The new system has significantly increased waiting time.

(b) H_o: $\mu \leqslant \mu_o \leqslant 6$

H_1: $\mu > \mu_o > 6$

A directional hypothesis is justified since Harriet is only interested in whether waiting time is *increased*.

$$z = \frac{8.1 - 6}{0.22} = 9.54$$

Reject H_o. There is a significant increase in waiting time.

(c) H_o: $\mu_1 = \mu_2$

H_1: $\mu_1 \neq \mu_2$

There is no basis for predicting which system is better.

$$z = \frac{8.1 - 7.2}{0.35} = 2.57$$

Reject H_o. There is a significant difference between the two systems.

132

8-15. (a) z-statistic, one-sample case since $n > 30$.
(b) Directional hypothesis since he wishes to examine only hypotheses consistent with fraud.
(c) $$z = \frac{16.23 - 0}{1.07} = 15.17$$

Reject H_o. It appears quite definite that the errors are biased in favor of the credit card company.

(d) Rincon has provided reasonably conclusive evidence that the results were unlikely to be due to chance or random variations of a random variable. Thus, the results are consistent with fraud. However, other factors (such as a program error) could cause a consistent direction of error.

8-19. (a) Student t-test, one-sample case.
(b) One-tailed since the interest is specifically in assessing the possible deleterious effects of the heat wave and drought.
(c) $t = -3.75$. The critical value of t at $\alpha = 0.01$, df = 24, one-tail test is -2.492. Since obtained t is in the critical region, we reject H_o and assert that the drought and heat wave has significantly reduced the yield of cotton per acre.

8-21. (a) Student t for significance of the difference between independent means.
(b) directional
(c) $$s\overline{X}_1 \text{-} \overline{X}_2 = \sqrt{\frac{20(0.15)^2 + 23(0.05)^2}{(20)(23)}} = 0.033$$

$t = 14.545$, df = 41

Although the critical value of t at df = 41 is not shown in the table, the t-ratio would clearly be in the critical region even at df = 40. We may reject H_o and assert that the concentrations of uranium in the ore of northeastern states is significantly higher than those of western states.

8-23. $H_o: \mu \geqslant 37\%$

$H_1: \mu < 37\%$

A one-tailed test is appropriate since his assertion is not that rate increases are different but *specifically* that they are *lower* for commodities other than furniture.

$$z = \frac{32 - 35}{1.74} = -1.72$$

We reject H_o since our obtained z falls in the critical region, i.e., $- 1.72 < -1.645$.

8-25. (a) z, since both n's exceed 30 and the Central Limit theorem applies.
(b) directional
(c) $$s\overline{X}_1 \text{-} \overline{X}_2 = \sqrt{\frac{35(16.43) + 31(14.99)}{35(31)}} = \sqrt{0.9583} = 0.9789$$

$$z = \frac{2.91}{0.9789} = 2.97$$

Reject H_o. The new equipment produces statistically significant gains in the mean percentage of pesticides detected.

8-27. All of the problems involve non-directional tests. The research is of the "let's find out" type rather than a test of a prior notion or hypothesis.

(a) $s_{\bar{p}} = 0.0414$, $z = -2.42$. We do not reject H_o. Note, had we set the α level at 0.05, we would have rejected H_o. Further study of this condition appears warranted.

(b) $s_{\bar{p}} = 0.0371$, $z = 1.35$. We do not reject H_o.

(c) $p = 0.4844$, $q = 0.5156$, $s_{\bar{p}_1-\bar{p}_2} = 0.0127$, $z = -11.80$. The z-statistic is in the lower region of rejection. A significantly greater proportion of smokers prefer the 0.15 mg. of tar cigarette to the one containing 0.1 mg. of tar.

8-29. (a) $\bar{p}_1 = 0.5389$, $\bar{q}_1 = 0.4611$, $s_{\bar{p}} = 0.0166$, $z = 2.34$. Using a two-tailed test, the critical value of $z > |1.96|$. We reject H_o. More than 50 percent of the east coast members prefer direct wage increases.

(b) $\bar{p}_2 = 0.5795$, $\bar{q}_2 = 0.4205$, $s_{\bar{p}} = 0.0166$, $z = 4.79$. Using a two-tailed test, reject H_o. More than 50 percent of the west coast members also prefer direct wage increases.

(c) $p = 0.5590$, $q = 0.4410$, $s_{\bar{p}_1-\bar{p}_2} = 0.0235$, $z = -1.73$. Using a two-tailed test, we do not reject H_o. There is not a significant difference between east and west coast union members on this issue.

8-31. H_o: $P = P_o = 0.40$

H_1: $P \neq P_o \neq 0.40$

Our hypotheses are non-directional since there is no basis for predicting a specific direction; therefore, we use a two-tailed test.

$$z = \frac{0.59 - 0.40}{0.0126} = 15.08$$

We reject H_o since our obtained z exceeds the critical value. The population in California appears to be significantly different from the rest of the country with respect to the proportion of "recession-proof spenders."

Chapter 9

9-5. (a)

	Plane	Auto	Train
Clear	14.00	24.50	35.00
Rain	6.25	10.00	13.25
Fog	3.00	2.80	2.70
Expected payoff	23.25	37.30	50.95

Taking a plane provides the maximum expected payoff (i.e., minimum expected time).

(b)

	Plane	Auto	Train
Clear	0	10.50	21.00
Rain	0	3.75	7.00
Fog	0.30	0.10	0
E(OL)	0.30	14.35	28.00

Taking a plane yields minimum expected opportunity loss.

(c) EVPI = 14.00 + 6.25 + 2.70 = 22.95

9-7. (a)

	#1	#2	#3
Expected income	1,900	2,250	2,375

Bob should buy Building #3.

(b) EVPI = 2787.50 - 2375 = 412.50

(c) Revised probabilities

P_1	P_2	P_3	P_4
0.6667	0.1531	0.0962	0.0538
0.1429	0.7653	0.0385	0.0645
0.0952	0.0306	0.8173	0.0215
0.0952	0.0510	0.0481	0.8602

(d)

	#1	#2	#3
P_1	2876.30	3571.65	4357.47
P_2	2420.50	3030.75	3546.12
P_3	1582.94	1774.35	1661.42
P_4	711.90	467.85	-298.22

9-9. (a) Revised probabilities

P_1	P_2	P_3	P_4
1.00	0	0	0
0	1.00	0	0
0	0	1.00	0
0	0	0	1.00

(b) EVSI = 2787.50 - 2375.00 = 412.50

The reason the EVSI = EVPI is because, in this case, we have perfect information.

9-11.

Proportion Defective	Conditional Probability $n = 30, x = 3$	Joint p	Revised p	Expected Cost of Accept	Expected Cost of Reject
0.01	0.0031	0.0014	0.0496	0.99	7.44
0.02	0.0188	0.0047	0.1667	6.67	25.00
0.03	0.0482	0.0072	0.2553	15.32	38.30
0.04	0.0863	0.0086	0.3050	24.00	0
0.05	0.1270	0.0063	0.2234	22.34	0
		0.0282		69.32	70.74

Accept the shipment since the expected cost of rejection is still greater than the expected cost of acceptance.

9-13.

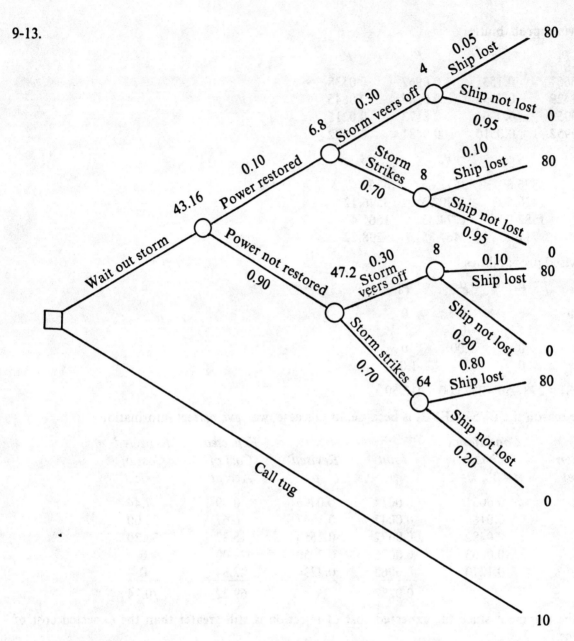

Thus, he should call the tugboat since the loss (10 million) is less than the loss of 43.16 million.

9-21. Find the expected cost of acceptance and rejection of two values of x (e.g., x = 0, x = 3) and plot these on a graph.

Proportion of Defectives	Prior p	Conditional Probability $(x = 0, n = 15)$	Joint p	Revised p	Expected Cost of Accept	Expected Cost of Reject
0.01	0.90	0.8601	0.7741	0.9955	3.87	74.66
0.20	0.10	0.0352	0.0035	0.0045	0.45	0.34
			0.7776		4.32	75.00

Proportion of Defectives	Prior p	Conditional Probability $(x = 3, n = 15)$	Joint p	Revised p	Expected Cost of Accept	Expected Cost of Reject
0.01	0.90	0.0004	0.0001	0.0040	0.02	0.30
0.20	0.10	0.2501	0.0250	0.9960	99.60	74.70
			0.0251		99.62	75.00

9-23. (a) Payoff table

		Buy 1,000	Buy 2,000	Buy 3,000
	1,000	14,000	3,000	-8,000
Sell	2,000	14,000	28,000	17,000
	3,000	14,000	28,000	42,000

(b) Maximin: Buy 1,000
Maximax: Buy 3,000

(c) Expected monetary gain: 1,000 = 14,000
2,000 = 15,500
3,000 = 9,500

He should buy 2,000.

(d) E(OL): 1,000 = 9,800
2,000 = 8,300
3,000 = 14,300

He should buy 2,000.

(e) EVPI = 23,800 - 15,500 = 8,300

9-25. (a) Revised probabilities

1,000	2,000	3,000
0.7143	0.4545	0.2830
0.1714	0.3896	0.3396
0.1143	0.1558	0.3774

(b) $p(P_{1,000}) = 0.35$; $p(P_{2,000}) = 0.385$; $p(P_{3,000}) = 0.265$

(c) 1,000; 2,000; 2,000

(d) EVSI = 16,849.48 - 15,500 = 1,349.48.

The value of the information is not worth the $1,500 fee; therefore, he should choose the first firm.

137

9-33.

Payoff (Costs) for Insurance Problem			
Event	Decision: Amount of Insurance Purchased		
	$ 0	$500,000	$1,000,000
No fire	0	1,400	2,100
Fire	1,000,000	501,400	2,100

(a)

Expected Value of Decision Amount of Insurance Purchased				
		0	500,000	1,000,000
	p	Expected Value	Expected Value	Expected Value
No fire	0.999	$(0)(0.999) = 0$	$(1,400)(0.999) = 1,398.6$	$(2,100)(0.999) = 2,097.9$
Fire	0.001	$(1,000,000)(0.999) = \underline{1,000}$ $1,000$	$(501,400)(0.001) = \underline{501.4}$ $1,900.0$	$(2,100)(0.001) = \underline{2.1}$ $2,100.0$

(b) The expected value of her loss was lowest when no insurance was purchased and highest when full coverage was obtained. Hence, by the expected monetary value criterion she should opt for no coverage. However, in the event of a fire, she would be financially bankrupt unless she had the highest coverage. Since her liquid assets were more than sufficient to cover the cost of the insurance, she would probably elect to obtain full coverage.

10-1. (a) $\Sigma X_{tot} = 86.8$; $\Sigma X^2_{tot} = 427.36$; $\dfrac{(\Sigma X_{tot})^2}{21} = 358.77$

$SS_{tot} = 68.60$, df = 20

$SS_{bet} = 7.17$, df = 2

$SS_w = 24.07 + 16.92 + 20.43 = 61.42$, df = 18

Source of Variation	df	Sum of Squares	Variance Est.	F
Between	2	7.17	3.585	1.05
Within	18	61.42	3.41	
Total	20	68.60*		

*Discrepancy of 0.01 due to rounding error.

Since obtained F is less than the critical value of F, we cannot reject H_o. The different processes do not appear to yield differing amounts of gold ore.

(b) The use of the Tukey test is not warranted.

10-3. (a) $\Sigma X_{tot} = 321$ $\Sigma X^2_{tot} = 2,471$

$SS_{tot} = 753.65$, df = 59

$SS_{bet} = 384.58$, df = 3

$SS_w = 104.93 + 95.60 + 70.93 + 97.60 = 369.06$, df = 56

Source of Variation	df	Sum of Squares	Variance Est.	F
Between	3	384.58	128.19	19.45
Within	56	369.06	6.59	
Total	59	753.65*		

*Slight disparity due to rounding error.

Referring to Table VIII, we find that there is no tabled value for F at 3 and 56 degrees of freedom. However, since obtained F exceeds the value of F required to reject H_o at 3 and 55 df (i.e., F = 4.16), we may reject H_o. Linear interpolation is not required in this case because, at 3 and 56 df, a smaller critical value of F is required for rejecting H_o.

(b)

		$\bar{X}_1$	$\bar{X}_2$	$\bar{X}_3$	$\bar{X}_4$
		4.27	9.60	2.93	4.60
$\bar{X}_1$	4.27	-	5.33*	1.34	0.33
$\bar{X}_2$	9.60	-	-	6.67*	5.00*
$\bar{X}_3$	2.93	-	-	-	1.67
$\bar{X}_4$	4.60	-	-	-	-

Using linear interpolation to find q_α at 56df and k = 4 and α = 0.01, we find:

$$4.59 + \frac{16}{20}(4.70 - 4.59) = 4.68$$

$$HSD = 4.68 \sqrt{\frac{6.59}{15}} = 3.10$$

The differences that achieve statistical significance are indicated by an asterisk in the above table. Note that machine X_2 produces significantly higher numbers of defectives than machines X_1, X_3, and X_4.

(b) SS_{tot} = 250, df = 62

SS_{bet} = 1,542.29 - 1,372 = 170.29, df = 8

SS_A = 1,419.24 - 1,372 = 47.24, df = 2

SS_B = 1,486.67 - 1,372 = 114.67, df = 2

SS_{AxB} = 170.29 - (47.24 + 114.67) = 8.38, df = 4

SS_w = 250 - 170.29 = 79.71, df = 54

Source of Variation	df	Sums of Squares	Variance Est.	F
Between-group	8	170.29		
A-variable	2	47.24	23.62	15.96
B-variable	2	114.67	57.34	38.74
A x B	4	8.38	2.10	1.42
Within-group	54	79.71	1.48	
Total	62	250.00		

Since the obtained F of both the A and B variables exceed the critical value at 2 and 50 df, it is unnecessary to interpolate between 50 and 55. We reject H_o with respect to both variables. Thus, amount of root hormone and amount of water affect the output of alfalfa.

(c) The HSD multicomparison test is warranted.

		A_1	A_2	A_3			B_1	B_2	B_3
		3.52	4.86	5.62			3.24	4.29	6.48
A_1	3.52	-	1.34*	2.10*	B_1	3.24	-	1.05	3.24*
A_2	4.86	-	-	0.76	B_2	4.29	-	-	2.19*
A_3	5.62	-	-	-	B_3	6.48	-	-	-

$$\text{HSD} = 4.41* \sqrt{\frac{1.48}{21}} = 1.17$$

(*By linear interpolation.)

Comparisons between A_1 and A_2 and A_1 vs A_3 are statistically significant. Both comparisons involving B_3 are statistically significant.

10-7. (a) Randomized block design.

(b) $\Sigma X_{tot} = 195.74$; $\Sigma X^2_{tot} = 2{,}260.21$; $\dfrac{(\Sigma X_{tot})^2}{n} = 2{,}128.56$

$SS_{tot} = 2{,}260.21 - 2{,}128.56 = 131.65$

$SS_{blks} = 2{,}187.42 - 2{,}128.56 = 58.56$

$SS_{treat} = 2{,}159.76 - 2{,}128.56 = 31.20$

Source of Var.	df	Sum of Squares	Var. Est.	F
Blocks	5	58.56	11.77	2.83
Treatments	2	31.20	15.60	3.75
Error	10	41.59	4.16	
Total	17	131.65		

Since neither of the obtained F statistics exceed the critical values for $\alpha = 0.05$ for the appropriate degrees of freedom, we fail to reject the null hypotheses.

10-9. (b) $SS_{tot} = 1{,}025.37$, df = 29

$SS_{bet} = 250.17$, df = 5

$SS_A = 4.87$

$SS_B = 166.64$

$SS_{AxB} = 78.66$

$SS_w = 775.2$, df = 24

Source of Variation	df	Sum of Squares	Variance Est.	F
Between group	5	250.17		
A-variable	2	4.87	2.44	0.08
B-variable	1	166.64	166.64	5.16
A x B	2	78.66	39.33	1.22
Within-group	24	775.20	32.30	
Total	29	1,025.37		

None of the differences is significant at the 0.01 level.

(c) Since no differences have been found to be significant, a multicomparison test is not warranted.

10-11. $\Sigma X_{tot} = 547.7$ $\qquad$ $\Sigma X^2_{tot} = 22,006.16$ $\qquad$ $\dfrac{(\Sigma X_{tot})^2}{n} = 19,976.45$

Source of Var.	df	Sum of Squares	Var. Est.	F
Blocks	4	748.46	187.12	1.81
Treatments	2	453.72	226.86	2.19
Error	8	827.53	103.44	
Total	14	2,029.71		

Neither F is significant.

10-13. (b)

$\Sigma X_{tot} = 16.85$ $\qquad$ $\Sigma X^2_{tot} = 68.1967$ $\qquad$ $\dfrac{(\Sigma X_{tot})^2}{n} = 9.4641$

Sums $\qquad$ $A_1 = 2.19$ $\qquad\qquad$ $A_2 = 16.93$ $\qquad\qquad$ $A_2 = -2.27$

$\qquad\qquad$ $B_1 = -4.95$ $\qquad\qquad$ $B_2 = 21.8$

Source of Var.	df	Sums of Squares	Var. Est.	F
Between	5	45.7915		
A	2	20.1933	10.0967	18.73*
B	1	15.5230	15.5230	28.79*
A x B	2	10.0752	5.0376	9.34*
Within	24	12.9411	0.5392	
Total	29	58.7326		

*Significant at $\alpha = 0.05$

10-15.

$\Sigma X_{tot} = 71.08$ $\qquad$ $\Sigma X^2_{tot} = 215.3888$ $\qquad$ $\dfrac{(\Sigma X_{tot})^2}{n} = 210.5153$

Sums: $A_1 = 25.01$ $\quad$ $A_2 = 20.36$ $\quad$ $A_3 = 25.71$ $\quad$ $B_1 = 39.06$ $\quad$ $B_2 = 32.02$

Source of Var.	df	Sums of Squares	Var. Est.	F
Between	5	4.34		
A	2	2.11	1.055	35.17*
B	1	2.07	2.07	69.00*
A x B	2	0.16	0.08	2.67
Within	18	0.53	0.03	
Total	23	4.87		

*Significant at $\alpha = 0.05$

11-1.

# females	f_o	p	f_e	$\frac{(f_o - f_e)^2}{f_e}$
0	84	0.0625	75	1.0800
1	317	0.2500	300	0.9633
2	449	0.3750	450	0.0022
3	283	0.2500	300	0.9633
4	67	0.0625	75	1.0800
	1,200		1,200	4.0888

df = 5 - 1 -1 = 3. Critical value of χ^2 = 7.815. Since obtained χ^2 is less than the critical value, we do not reject H_o. The data conform to expectations based on a binomial distribution in which P = 0.50. Note: by census count, the actual proportion of females has averaged 0.4849 over recent years.

11-3.

Changes	z-Scores	Proportion	f_e
-20 to under -15	-2.15 to -1.60	0.0548	3.56
-15 to under -10	-1.60 to -1.05	0.0921	5.99
-10 to under -5	-1.05 to -0.50	0.1616	10.50
-5 to under 0	-0.50 to 0.05	0.2114	13.74
0 to under 5	0.05 to 0.60	0.2058	13.38
5 to under 10	0.60 to 1.15	0.1492	9.70
10 to under 15	1.15 to 1.69	0.0796	5.17
15 to under 20	1.69 to 2.24	0.0455	2.96
		1.0000	65.00

> 9.55 (first two rows); > 8.13 (last two rows)

χ^2 = 3.768, df = 6 - 1 - 2 = 3. Accept H_o.

11-5. (a) Favoring or opposing a strike vote is independent of years of membership in the union.

(b) df = 3

(c)

Years of Membership	Favor	Oppose	
0 - under 5	f_o = 25, f_e = 46.89	f_o = 10, f_e = 18.11	35
5 - under 10	f_o = 40, f_e = 45.83	f_o = 55, f_e = 49.17	95
10 - under 15	f_o = 30, f_e = 27.98	f_o = 28, f_e = 30.02	58
15 and over	f_o = 15, f_e = 19.30	f_o = 25, f_3 = 20.70	40
	110	118	228

χ^2 = 3.8941 + 3.6318 + 0.7416 + 0.6913 + 0.1458 + 0.1359 + 0.9580 + 0.8932 = 11.0917

The critical value at α = 0.01 and df = 3 is 11.341. Since obtained χ^2 falls short of this value, we cannot reject H_o.

11-13.

Grade of Ore	f_o	p	f_e	$\dfrac{(f_o - f_e)^2}{f_e}$
High	10	0.0323	9.69	0.0099
Medium high	30	0.0645	19.35	5.8616
Medium	50	0.1290	38.70	3.2995
Medium low	80	0.2581	77.43	0.0853
Low	130	0.5161	154.83	3.9820
	300	1.0000	300.00	13.2383

df = 5 - 1 - 1 = 3. Critical value is 7.815. Since obtained χ^2 exceeds critical value, we reject H_o. Apparently, the frequency of various grades of ore do not follow the hypothesized distribution.

11-17.

	Under 25	*25 and over*
f_o	1159	1694
f_e	1312.98	1540.62

$\chi^2 = 17.926 + 15.270 = 33.196$, df = 1

Reject H_o. A smaller proportion of individuals below 25 years age attended films dealing with mature adult relationships than would be expected under H_o.

11-21. (a) $\chi^2 = \dfrac{(342-241)^2}{241} + \dfrac{(140-241)^2}{241} = 84.656$

A greater proportion of males than females was attracted to *North Dallas Forty*.

(b) $\chi^2 = \dfrac{(111-173.5)^2}{173.5} + \dfrac{(236-173.5)^2}{173.5} = 45.029$

A greater proportion of females than males was attracted to *Promises in the Dark*.

11-23. Sign test n = 23, x = 24

$\mu = nP = 33(0.50) = 16.5$

$\sigma = \sqrt{(33)(0.50)(0.50)} = 2.87$

$z = \dfrac{24 - 16.5}{2.87} = 2.61$

We may reject H_o and assert that there is a difference in hourly earnings between workers in tobacco and textile industries.

11-29. $U_1 = (18)(25) + \dfrac{18(19)}{2} - 359 = 262$

$U_2 = (18)(25) + \dfrac{25(26)}{2} - 587 = 188$

$\mu_u = \dfrac{(18)(25)}{2} = 225$

$\sigma_u = \sqrt{\dfrac{(18)(25)(44)}{12}} = 40.62$

$z = \dfrac{262 - 225}{40.62} = 0.91$ Accept H_o

11-13.

		Male	Female	
Respondents	f_e	201,108	25,362	226,470
Non-respondents	f_e	101,491	12,799	114,290
		302,599	38,161	340,760

$\chi^2 = 1.034 + 2.049 + 8.199 = 27.528$, df = 1   Reject H_o.

11-33.

Males f_e	Females f_e
15,087.2	1,912.8
1,597.5	202.5
24,583.3	3,116.7
41,356.7	5,243.3
9,229.8	1,170.2
43,131.7	5,468.3
13,134.8	1,665.2
7,987.4	1,012.6
52,272.8	6,627.2
35,233.1	4,466.9
44,196.7	5,603.3

$\chi^2 = 23,854.263$ Reject H_o. The proportion of men and women is not independent of field.

11-37. Sign test. n = 33, x = 21. μ = 16.5, σ = 2.87

$$z = \frac{21 - 16.5}{2.87} = 1.57$$

There is no statistical basis for asserting that the proportion of credit liquidated differs for automobile loans versus total credit.

11-39. (a)   Sign test. DJ Transp. vs DJ util. n_+ = 41, n_- = 24

$$\mu = 65(0.50) = 32.5$$

$$\sigma = \sqrt{(65)(0.50)(0.50)} = 4.03$$

$$z = \frac{41 - 32.5}{4.03} = 2.11$$

Reject H_o. The changes in the DJ Transp. are significantly greater (higher) than changes in DJ util.

(b)   Sign test. DJ transp. vs. futures. n_+ = 26, n_- = 39

$$z = \frac{26 - 32.5}{4.03} = -1.61.$$

Accept H_o. No statistical basis for asserting that changes in the DJ transp. differs from changes in DJ futures.

(c)   Sign test. DJ util vs DJ futures. n_+ = 22, n_- = 43

$$z = \frac{22 - 32.5}{4.03} = -2.61.$$

Reject H_o and assert that changes in the DJ futures are significantly higher than changes in DJ util.

Chapter 12

12-7. (a) $X = 15$, $Y_c = 10.81$

$s_{y_c} = 1.25$; 95% confidence interval: 8.02 to 13.60

(b) $s_{y\,ind} = 3.69$; 95% predictive interval: 2.59 to 19.03

(c)   The interval estimates for $X = 15$ are wider than the corresponding intervals for $X = 10$. This is because $X = 10$ is much closer to the mean of X.

12-9.
$$\Sigma X = 27.23 \qquad \Sigma Y = 27.52$$
$$\Sigma X^2 = 102.0683 \qquad \Sigma Y^2 = 103.4526$$
$$\overline{X} = 3.40 \qquad \overline{Y} = 3.44$$

$$\Sigma XY = 101.5486$$

$$r = \frac{101.58 - \dfrac{(27.23)(27.52)}{8}}{\sqrt{\left[102.0683 - \dfrac{(27.23)^2}{8}\right]\left[103.4526 - \dfrac{(27.52)^2}{8}\right]}}$$

$$= \frac{7.8774}{9.0790}$$

$$= 0.87$$

12-11. (a)

$$r = \frac{17{,}032.07 - \dfrac{(1985.84)(326.03)}{40}}{\sqrt{\left[103{,}885.46 - \dfrac{(1985.84)^2}{40}\right]\left[3759.30 - \dfrac{(326.03)^2}{40}\right]}}$$

$$= \frac{845.9846}{2415.8256}$$

$$= 0.35$$

12-13. (12.10) $r = 0.21$, $n = 40$

$s_r = 0.1586$

$t = \dfrac{0.21}{0.1586} = 1.324$ Accept H_o

(12.11) $r = 0.35$, $n = 40$

$t = \dfrac{0.35}{0.1520} = 2.303$ Reject H_o

We may not conclude that a cause and effect relationship exists. We have merely demonstrated that both variables tend to move in the same direction; i.e., high volume is associated with larger changes and low volume with smaller changes.

12-15. (c)

$$\Sigma X = 76.9 \qquad \Sigma Y = 162.8 \qquad a = 9.05$$
$$\Sigma X^2 = 449.25 \qquad \Sigma Y^2 = 1902.98 \qquad b = 0.47$$
$$\overline{X} = 5.49 \qquad \overline{Y} = 11.63$$

$$\Sigma XY = 906.83 \quad n = 14$$

$$r^2 = \frac{9.05(162.8) + (0.47)(906.83) - (14)(11.63)^2}{1902.98 - 14(11.63)^2}$$

$$= \frac{5.9535}{9.3834}$$

$$= 0.6345$$

(d) $r = \sqrt{0.6345}$

$$= 0.80$$

(e)

$$t = \sqrt{\frac{0.80}{\frac{(1-0.8^2)}{12}}} = 4.619$$

The critical value of t for df = 12, $\alpha = 0.01$, two-tailed test, is 3.055. Thus, we reject H_o and assert that there is a positive relationship between unemployment rates and suicide rates.

(f)

$$s_{y.x} = \sqrt{\frac{\Sigma Y^2 - a\Sigma Y - b\Sigma XY}{n - 2}}$$

$$= \sqrt{\frac{1902.98 - 9.05(162.8) - 0.47(906.83)}{12}}$$

$$= 0.53$$

(g) $s_{y_c} = 0.29$; X = 8.0, $Y_c = 12.81$; 95% confidence interval: 12.18 to 13.44

(h) $S_b = 0.102$; $t = \dfrac{0.47}{0.102} = 4.608$ \qquad Reject H_o.

12-17. (b)

$$\Sigma X = 33{,}578 \qquad \Sigma Y = 333$$
$$\Sigma X^2 = 98{,}706{,}204 \qquad \Sigma Y^2 = 9{,}735$$
$$\overline{X} = 2{,}798.17$$

$$\Sigma XY = 891{,}070 \quad n = 12$$

$$b = -0.009, \ a = 51.74$$

$$Y_c = 51.74 - 0.009X$$

(c) $s_{y.x} = \sqrt{\dfrac{9{,}735 - 51.74(333) + 0.009(891{,}070)}{10}} = 7.25$

(d) $s_b = 0.003$ \quad $t = \dfrac{-0.009}{0.003} = -3.00$ \quad Reject H_o

12-19. $X = 2,500$, $Y_c = 29.24$

(a)
$$s_{y_c} = s_{y.x} \sqrt{\frac{1}{n} + \frac{(X - \bar{X})^2}{\Sigma X^2 - \frac{(\Sigma X)^2}{n}}}$$

$$= 7.25 \sqrt{\frac{1}{12} + \frac{(2,500 - 2,798.17)^2}{98,706,204 - \frac{(33,578)^2}{12}}}$$

$$= 7.25 \sqrt{0.0833 + \frac{88,905.3489}{4,749,363.667}} = 2.32$$

95% confidence interval: $29.24 \pm (2.228)(2.32)$
29.24 ± 5.17 or 24.07 to 34.41

(b)
$$s_{y_{ind}} = s_{y.x} \sqrt{1 + \frac{1}{n} + \frac{(X - \bar{X})^2}{\Sigma X^2 - \frac{(\Sigma X)^2}{n}}}$$

$$= 7.25 \sqrt{1 + .1020} = 7.61$$

95% predictive interval:

$29.24 \pm (2.228)(7.61)$
± 16.96 or
12.28 to 46.20

12-21. (b)

$\Sigma X = 245$ $\Sigma Y = 57.7$
$\Sigma X^2 = 6,113$ $\Sigma Y^2 = 313.43$
$\bar{X} = 22.27$ $n = 11$

$\Sigma XY = 1365.4$

$b = 0.12$, $a = 2.52$, $Y_c = 2.52 + 0.12X$

(d)
$$s_{y.x} = \sqrt{\frac{313.43 - 2.52(57.7) - 0.12(1365.4)}{9}}$$

$$= 0.68$$

$$s_b = s_{y.x} \sqrt{\frac{1}{\Sigma X^2 - \frac{(\Sigma X)^2}{n}}}$$

$$= 0.68 \, (0.039)$$

$$= 0.0265$$

$$t = \frac{b}{s_b} = \frac{0.12}{0.0265} = 4.528$$

Reject H_o

12-25. $\Sigma X = 192.73$ $\Sigma Y = 210.79$
$\Sigma X^2 = 2207.3475$ $\Sigma Y^2 = 2722.5333$
$\overline{X} = 11.34$ $\overline{Y} = 12.40$

$\Sigma XY = 2397.6378$ $n = 17$

$b = 0.35$
$a = 8.43$

(a) $Y_c = 8.43 + 0.35X$

Chapter 14

14-3. (a) $x = 0$ for 1964

x	Y_t		
-15	29.6	$\Sigma Y = 470$	
12	38.6	$\Sigma xY = -191.4$	
-9	45.5	$\Sigma x^2Y = 34{,}066.8$	
-6	50.3		
-3	52.9	$\Sigma x^2 = 990$	
0	53.4	$\Sigma x^4 = 158{,}598$	
3	51.7		
6	48.0		
9	42.1	$470 = 11a + 990c$	
12	34.0	$34{,}066.8 = 990a + 158{,}598c$	
15	23.8		

$a = 53.3893$
$b = -0.1933$
$c = -0.1185$

$Y_t = 53.3893 - 0.1933x - 0.1185x^2$

14-5.

Year	% Trend
1967	102.0
1968	100.3
1969	99.6
1970	99.6
1971	98.0
1972	95.5
1973	95.7
1974	100.2
1975	103.1
1976	103.0
1977	103.4

14-15. (a) n = 30   x = 0 for 1976 between III and IV quarter
                        (i.e., x = -1 1976 III quarter
                            x = 1 1976 IV quarter)

ΣX^2 = 8,990
Σx^4 = 4,842,014
ΣY = 433.80
ΣxY = 1,895.64
$\Sigma x^2 Y$ = 135,528.84

433.80 = 30a + 8,990c
135,528.84 = 8,990a + 4,842,014c

a = 13.6809
b = 0.2109
c = 0.0026

$\hat{Y}_t = 13.6809 + 0.2109x + 0.0026x^2$

(b)

	Y_t		Y_t
1973	9.75	1977	14.34
	9.88		14.80
	10.03		15.28
	10.21		15.79
1974	10.40	1978	16.32
	10.61		16.86
	10.85		17.43
	11.10		18.02
1975	11.38	1979	18.63
	11.68		19.26
	11.99		19.91
	12.33		20.58
1976	12.69	1980	21.27
	13.07		21.98
	13.47		
	13.89		

(c) The trend values represent the billions of dollars for new plant and equipment for a given quarter had seasonal, cyclical, and irregular factors not been present.

14-17.

			Four-Quarter Moving Total	Eight-Quarter Moving Total	(a) Moving Aver.	(c) $\frac{Y}{MA}$ x 100	(e) SI	(f) $\frac{Y}{SI}$ x 100
1973	I	18.56					93.9	19.77
	II	22.10					96.9	22.80
	III	29.56	96.96	200.34	25.04	118.05	105.7	27.97
	IV	26.74	103.38	215.74	26.97	99.15	103.6	25.81
1974	I	24.98	112.36	230.18	28.77	86.83	93.9	26.60
	II	31.08	117.82	236.46	29.56	105.14	96.9	32.07
	III	35.02	118.64	232.41	29.05	120.55	105.7	33.13
	IV	27.56	113.77	213.07	26.63	103.49	103.6	26.60
1975	I	20.11	99.30	183.55	22.94	87.66	93.9	21.42
	II	16.61	84.25	158.73	19.84	83.72	96.9	17.14
	III	19.97	74.48	144.10	18.01	110.88	105.7	18.89
	IV	17.79	69.62	138.96	17.37	102.42	103.6	17.17
1976	I	15.25	69.34	134.81	16.85	90.50	93.9	16.24
	II	16.33	65.47	127.73	15.97	102.25	96.9	16.85
	III	16.10	62.26	123.71	15.46	104.14	105.7	15.23
	IV	14.58	61.45	122.08	15.25	95.61	103.6	14.07
1977	I	14.44	60.63	122.63	15.33	94.19	93.9	15.38
	II	15.51	62.00	129.17	16.15	96.04	96.9	16.01
	III	17.47	67.17	140.37	17.59	99.32	105.7	16.53
	IV	19.75	73.20	152.88	19.11	103.34	103.6	19.06
1978	I	20.47	79.68	166.43	20.80	98.41	93.9	21.80
	II	21.99	86.75	184.15	2302	95.53	96.9	22.69
	III	24.54	97.40	204.57	25.57	95.97	105.7	23.22
	IV	30.40	107.17	222.02	27.75	109.55	103.6	29.34
1979	I	30.24	114.85	237.47	29.68	101.89	93.9	32.20
	II	29.67	122.62	255.12	31.89	93.04	96.9	30.62
	III	32.31	132.50	268.86	33.61	96.13	105.7	30.57
	IV	40.28	136.36	276.59	34.57	116.52	103.6	38.88
1980	I	34.26	140.23	277.71	34.71	98.70	93.9	36.49
	II	33.54	137.48	274.59	34.32	97.73	96.9	34.61
	III	29.56	137.11				105.7	27.97
	IV	39.91					103.6	38.52

14-19. Domestic imports—cigarettes

Year	x	Y	$\log Y$	$x \log Y$
1973	-5	250	2.3979	-11.9895
1974	-3	301	2.4786	-7.4358
1975	-1	368	2.5658	-2.5658
1976	1	510	2.7076	2.7076
1977	3	615	2.7889	8.3667
1978	5	749	2.8745	14.3725
Sums			15.8133	3.4557

$$\Sigma x^2 = 70$$

$$\log a = \frac{15.8133}{6} = 2.6356 \qquad a = 432.1$$

$$\log b = \frac{3.4557}{70} = 0.0494 \qquad b = 1.12$$

$$Y_t = (432.1)(1.12)^x \qquad x = 0 \text{ in } 1975\ 1/2$$

14-21.

	Forecast 1				Forecast 2			
	Actual Deviation	Absolute Deviation	Deviation Squared	RSFE	Actual Deviation	Absolute Deviation	Deviation Squared	RSFE
1	-40	40	1,600	-40	-360	360	129,600	-360
2	-470	470	220,900	-510	-430	430	184,900	-790
3	-890	890	792,100	-1,400	-410	410	168,100	-1,200
4	-1,300	1,300	1,690,000	-2,700	300	300	90,000	-900
5	-1,690	1,690	2,856,100	-4,390	110	110	12,100	-790
6	-2,070	2,070	4,284,900	-6,460	-170	170	28,900	-960
7	-2,440	2,440	5,953,600	-8,900	-540	540	291,600	-1,500
8	-2,800	2,800	7,840,000	-11,700	-1,000	1,000	1,000,000	-2,500
9	-3,150	3,150	9,922,500	-14,850	-1,550	1,550	2,402,500	-4,050
10	-3,460	3,460	11,971,600	-18,310	-2,170	2,170	4,708,900	-6,220
		15,510	45,533,300			7,040	9,016,600	

(a) $\quad MAD_1 = 1,551 \qquad\qquad\qquad MAD_2 = 704$

$$SAD_1 = \frac{45,533,300}{10} = 4,553,330 \qquad SAD_2 = \frac{9,016,600}{10} = 901,660$$

$$\frac{\text{tracking}}{\text{signal}} = \frac{-18,310}{1,551} = -11.81 \qquad \frac{\text{tracking}}{\text{signal}} = \frac{-6,220}{740} = -8.41$$

(b) Both forecasts overestimated the actual cost of repairs. However, since MAD and SAD were higher for Forecast 1 than Forecast 2, Forecast 2 appears to be superior. Moreover, the tracking signal for both forecasts suggests that both models are failing to accurately track the rising costs of repair services.

15-9. *Price in 1979*
       Price in 1793

$$\frac{210}{112} = 1,875$$

$$\frac{931}{382} = 2.437 \qquad \text{Simple average of relatives index} = \frac{7.721}{4} \times 100$$

$$\frac{322}{220} = 1.464 \qquad\qquad\qquad\qquad\qquad\qquad = 193$$

$$\frac{535}{275} = 1.945$$

$$\Sigma\left(\frac{P_n}{P_o}\right) = 7.721$$

15-27. (a) One possible procedure would be to divide the number of fatalities for each year by the average number of miners employed daily for that year, yielding an annual proportion per average daily worker. These proportions can then be transformed into index numbers, using 1960 as the base year.

(1) Year	*(2)* # Fatalities	*(3)* Average # Men Working Daily	*(4)* Proportion per Average # Employed Daily	*(5)* Index No.
1930	2,063	644	$\frac{2,063}{644} = 3.203$	187.2
1935	1,242	565	$\frac{1,242}{565} = 2.198$	128.5
1940	1,388	533	$\frac{1,388}{533} = 2.604$	152.2
1945	1,068	438	$\frac{1,068}{438} = 2.438$	142.5
1950	643	483	$\frac{643}{483} = 1.331$	77.8
1955	448	260	$\frac{448}{260} = 1.732$	101.2
1960	325	190	$\frac{325}{190} = \boxed{1.711}$	100.0
1965	259	149	$\frac{259}{149} = 1.738$	101.6
1970	260	144	$\frac{260}{144} = 1.806$	105.6
1975	155	218	$\frac{155}{218} = 0.711$	41.6

(b) To obtain the weighted aggregate index shown in Column 5, we divide each proportion in Column 4 by 1.711 (proportion for base year 1960) and multiply by 100.

15-35.

P_o	P_n	Q_w
56.25	192.33	89,185.00
249.80	444.90	3,609.7
356.70	695.60	1,520.25
145.00	370.10	762.00
231.00	151.20	468.45

$$\frac{19,276,648.12}{6,692,726.685} = 288.0$$

Glossary of Terms

	Page
Aggregate index (composite index)	
an index that summarizes a group of items or components.	481
Alpha (α)	
The probability that nonchance factors are operating.	227
Alternative hypotheses (H_1)	
A statement that specifies that the population parameter is a value other than that specified in the null hypothesis.	225
Analysis of variance	
A statistical technique used for testing null hypotheses concerning two or more means.	298
Arithmetic mean	
Sum of the values of a variable divided by the number of observations.	51
Array	
Data that are ordered from either low to high or vice versa.	23
Average of relatives index	
An index in which we obtain separately the relative of each item or component and then find the mean of these relatives.	484
Base	
The price, quantity, or value of a period with which a given period is compared.	479
Bernoulli trials	
Experiments that can result in only one of two mutually exclusive and exhaustive outcomes.	122
Between-group sum of squares (SS_{bet})	
Deviations of each group mean from the grand mean, squared and summed.	302
Between-group variance estimate	
An independent estimate of the population variance based on the variability between the groups.	299
Bias	
A systematic type of error that does not balance out with continued sampling.	161
Binomial	
A family of theoretical distributions which follow the same mathematical rule for relating probabilities to values of a discrete random variable. Each distribution differs in specific probabilities according to n and P.	123
Binomial distribution	
A theoretical distribution that yields the probability of a given number of successes in n Bernoulli trials.	123

155

Census

The process by which we collect data on every element of the population.

Central-limit theorem

If random samples of a fixed n are drawn from any population (regardless of the form of the population distribution), as n becomes larger, the sampling distribution of means approaches normality.

Class limit

Upper or lower boundary of a class.

Classical approach to probability

The assignment of probability values on the basis of theoretical expectations in a hypothetical population.

Cluster sample

A sample in which the population is divided into naturally occurring groupings or clusters.

Coefficient of determination (r^2)

The ratio of explained variation to total variation.

Coefficient of multiple determination

Called Multiple R^2, it shows the proportion of the total variation in the dependent variable that is accounted for by the regression plane.

Coefficient of nondetermination (k^2)

Proportion of variation not accounted for in terms of the relationship between X and Y.

Complement

The complement of an outcome is its opposite.

Conditional distributions

The distribution of Y-values for any given value of X.

Conditional mean

The mean of the distribution of Y-values for any given X.

Conditional probability

The probability of an event given that another event has occurred. Symbolically, $p(A|B)$ is the probability of A given that B has occurred.

Confidence coefficient

The probability that the confidence interval will contain the population parameter. The most commonly used confidence coefficients are 0.95 and 0.99.

Confidence limits

The upper and lower boundaries of the confidence interval.

Consistent estimator

Contingency table

Continuous random variable

Continuous variables

Convenience sampling

Correlational analysis

Critical region

Critical value

Cumulative frequency distribution

Cyclical fluctuations

Data

Decision analysis

Decisions

Decisions made under certainty

Decisions made under uncertainty

Estimator

A statistic used to estimate or make inferences, about a parameter. Estimators include sample means variances, standard deviations, and proportions. 196

Event

A collection of specific sample points or outcomes. 89

Exhaustive

Outcomes are exhaustive if the sum of their separate probabilities is equal to 1.00. 84

Expansion

The rising phase of a business cycle. 454

Expected value

A form of weighted average in which the probabilities associated with each value of the random variable are used as weights; long-term average over many samples. 118

Expected value criterion

Choosing the alternative that leads to the maximum expected payoff in the long run. 259

Expected value of perfect information (EVPI)

The expected profit with perfect information minus the expected profit under uncertainty; sometimes called "the cost of uncertainty". 262

Expected value of sample information (EVSI)

The expected payoff with sample information minus the expected payoff with uncertainty. 278

Experiment

The process by which we obtain measurements or observations of different outcomes. 83

Explained variation

Variation of predicted scores from the sample mean $\Sigma(Y_c - \overline{Y})^2$. 403

Factorial design

A research design in which independent observations are obtained for each level of the treatment variables. We call each specific combination of experimental conditions the treatment combination. 311

F-distributions

A family of distributions distinguished by degrees of freedom associated with two different variance estimates. 300

F-ratio

The between-group variance estimate divided by the within-group variance estimate. 299

Finite correction factor (fcf)

A term used to reduce the size of the uncorrected standard error of the mean, when the ratio of sample size to population size $\left(\dfrac{n}{N}\right)$ is greater than 0.05. 180

Multiple correlation

A single value that describes the overall strength of the correlation between two or more independent variables and the dependent variables.

420

Multiple regression analysis

The process by which two or more independent variables are used to predict values of a dependent variable.

378

Two or more variables are used as predictor variables in regression analysis.

420

Mutually exclusive

Two events are said to be mutually exclusive if both occur simultaneously.

25

Two or more outcomes that cannot occur simultaneously.

84

Negatively skewed distribution

Frequency distribution with relatively fewer measurements occurring at the low end of the horizontal axis.

61

Non-directional hypothesis

An alternative hypothesis that states merely that the parameter is different from the one stated under H_o.

229

Non-parametric tests

Statistical tests that do not make assumptions about the shape of the parent or population distribution.

347

Non-sampling error

An error that is caused by the way in which the observations are made.

162

Normal approximation to binomial

A theoretical distribution used to approximate binomial probabilities when n is large and P approaches 0.5. When nP and nQ exceed 7, the normal distribution provides a reasonable approximation to binomial values.

145

Normal curve

Frequency distribution with a characteristic bell-shaped form.

61

Null hypothesis (H_o)

A statement that specifies hypothesized values for one or more of the population parameters. In a statistical test, the null hypothesis states the hypothesis to be tested. It often, but not necessarily, involves the hypothesis of "no effect".

224

Ogive

A chart of a cumulative frequency distribution.

36

One-tailed probability value

Probability value associated with directional hypotheses. The proportion of area in only one tail of the distribution is taken into account.

229

One-way analysis of variance

Statistical test of various categories or levels of a *single* treatment variable.

309

166